About the author.

George Nicholls is marr
Born in Sheffield, he lat
school in Kirby Lonsda entering the teaching profession he trained as a research chemist and served in the Royal Air Force. A graduate of London University, he moved from Deputy-Headmaster of an inner-city school to a succession of three Headships.

"Still Ahead", his second book and a sequel to Head's Tales (published by Hamilton & Co. Publishers Ltd.) was inspired by his work in teaching, supplemented by his experiences as a magistrate.

STILL AHEAD

Still Ahead

by

George Nicholls

CENTRAL PUBLISHING LIMITED.
West Yorkshire

Paperback ISBN 1 903970 02 4

Published
by

Central Publishing Limited.
Royd Street Offices
Milnsbridge
Huddersfield
West Yorkshire
HD3 4QY

www.centralpublishing.co.uk

Dedication

To Matthew for his meticulous attention to reading the proof.
To Carl for his sound advice on publicity and distribution.
To Chris for his expert technical assistance.
To Patrick for his invaluable help and support, which has made the production of my two books so much easier.

Foreword

'There is nothing more difficult to carry out, nor more doubtful of success, nor more dangerous to handle than to initiate a new order of things. For the reformer has enemies in all who profit by the old order, and only lukewarm defenders in all those who would profit by the new order, this lukewarmness arising partly from fear of their adversaries - and from the incredulity of mankind, who do not truly believe in anything new until they have had actual experience of it.'

Nicolo Machiavelli.

'Still Ahead' is the sequel to 'Head's Tales'. It is based on the same fundamental premise that misbehaviour in schools is perpetrated by a relatively small number of deviants who, nevertheless, will cause a disproportionate amount of disruption if their anti-social activities are not curbed.

Yet Adam Firestone's success in curtailing misconduct almost undermined him, the resulting increase in his school's popularity being reflected in the escalation in the numbers seeking admission to Lea Grange. This book tells how he adjusted to this meteoric growth, enabling him to continue with his personal involvement in maintaining the standard of control that is required in any place of learning.

The events described are based on similar, but not exact, incidents in the author's everyday work. Likewise, although the characters are based upon his experience, they are not precise descriptions of persons living or dead.

Of course, successful headmastership demands a multitude of skills over and above the ability to curtail misbehaviour. Thus, the situations described represent but a small part of the author's work. Similarly, the wayward characters depicted reflect only a tiny proportion of the thousands of well-behaved girls and boys whom he has been privileged to teach.

George Nicholls.

Still Ahead

CHAPTER ONE

'There is nothing more difficult to carry out, nor more doubtful of success, nor more dangerous to handle than to initiate a new order of things.'

Niccolo Machiavelli.

I had barely completed my daily entry into the school logbook, my last task before departing for the evening, when the telephone buzzed.

"Lea Grange School."

"Mr. Firestone?"

"Yes, speaking."

"Mr. Firestone, thank goodness it's you. Muriel Carruthers here. Mr. Firestone, we've got a problem."

Even before she announced herself, I had recognised the cut glass accent of a stalwart of the parents' association: a sober lady not normally given to melodrama. Thus, the anxious tone of her voice concerned me.

"A problem? With one of the twins?"

"No, no Mr. Firestone, not a family problem, a school problem. What I'm trying to say is that you've got a problem."

On that Friday evening, when I was anticipating a carefree weekend, the last thing I needed was for Muriel Carruthers to present me with a problem.

"A school problem! Right, let me have it and we'll see what can be done."

The line was silent. "Are you still there, Mrs. Carruthers?"

"Yes, I'm sorry. It's so embarrassing."

"Well you'll have to tell me what the problem is if I'm to sort it out."

"Yes, I know. Right. Here goes. When I came to pick up the twins this afternoon, one of your younger boys was behaving himself in a very naughty manner."

"Tell me more."

"Well, he was using one of those artificial things and pretending to expose himself."

Then suddenly, after an appreciable pause, during which we were both silent, she blurted, "At least...I think it was artificial!"...More silence, then, "Either that or he's a very lucky boy!"

I remember thinking, "There's no answer to that." Hastily I terminated the conversation, promising to investigate and to do the necessary chastising. In retrospect I pray that the telephone was secure in its cradle before my laughter exploded.

I was still shaking when Bill Brown, the school keeper, popped his head round my door to inform me that all was locked up and that he was on his way home.

"Are you all right Mr. Firestone?"

"Yes thanks Bill. I'll make sure the front door's secure when I leave. I'll be off in a few minutes."

In the quiet solitude of my study, my first impulse was to ask myself how on earth, only a few weeks earlier, I could have contemplated giving up this fascinating job to become a school inspector. What foolishness had possessed me to believe that the prestige associated with Her Majesty's Inspectorship of Schools could compete with the fulfilment and fun I derived, on a daily basis, from being Headmaster of Lea Grange School, Beckbridge, Lancashire?

I loved all aspects of my work but, in particular, I revelled in the achievements of my pupils.

My conviction that order and discipline are pre-requisites of a good school had not changed since the day I took up my post several years earlier. I was still in no doubt that scallywags had to be winkled out and dealt with before weak-minded individuals could copy their bad behaviour.

In those early years of headmastership, I was determined to

carve out time so that I could be in the vanguard of such operations. After all, my nickname as a boy had been C.I.D. Firestone. From a young age I had been fascinated by detective stories and I suppose I fancied myself as a latter-day Sherlock Holmes.

I could look back, over the past five years, at several incidents where my initiative had successfully scotched problems before the would-be perpetrators of evil had barely begun their dastardly deeds. And I had really enjoyed the challenges I had faced: the tracking down of Billy Gregory in the foothills of the Pennines; the exposing of the Black Hand Gang, albeit with the aid of my footballing friend, the parish priest; and the thwarting of Rupert's efforts to manufacture explosives. These were perhaps the most exciting skirmishes with deviants but there had been many others.

Five years on, I realised that my situation had changed appreciably. The numbers on roll at Lea Grange had increased year by year from under four hundred pupils, when I arrived, to just over one thousand. The administrative side of my duties was absorbing more and more of my time and I was concerned.

Unless I took immediate action, the growth of the school would dictate such a change in my work schedule that my personal contacts with pupils would be diminished and the time available for my 'hands-on' involvement in maintaining discipline would disappear.

Only a day earlier, I had been shocked with poignant confirmation that the fears I was harbouring were not without grounds. On my way to school that morning, I had run into a violent thunderstorm when I still had about a mile to travel. The downpour was so heavy that I decided to pull into the kerb to allow it to abate.

At that moment, a small boy in Lea Grange uniform hurried past, rapidly getting soaked to the skin. I wound down my window and called to him, "Jump in and I'll run you to school."

"No, thank you," he shouted over his shoulder as he hurried away.

Twenty minutes later, as I sat at my desk reviewing the day ahead, Paul Robson, my Deputy, popped his head round my door.

"Have you come in your wife's white Honda Accord?"

"Yes. Why do you ask?"

"Did you stop in St. Luke's Road?"

"Yes."

"Did you offer one of our new intake a lift?"

"I offered a lift to a small boy. He was wearing our uniform but I did not recognise him."

"Well, he obviously didn't recognise his Headmaster. He's asked me to report you to the police for trying to abduct him!"

I was appalled. Admittedly, it was only the second week of a new school year but I could not allow such a state of affairs to develop. I vowed to work out a solution.

I would have to improve my management skills. In particular, I would need to use my time more effectively. The key to this would be to plan carefully rather than allow events to take charge. The teachers must be involved more in the day to day running of the school and be clear about their responsibilities in this respect.

Fortunately, I had been thrown a lifeline in that the recent growth of Lea Grange had made us eligible for a second Deputy Head to work in tandem with Paul Robson, our first Deputy. I would be able to delegate a fair slice of my desk work to the pair of them and thereby free myself for the personal aspect of my job, the part that made going to work worthwhile. I had arranged the interviews for the following week. I could hardly wait!

Eventually, the big day dawned. "Mr. Firestone, I don't think you've seen the latest photograph of my pussy cat: she's such a little sweetie." Thus spoke Miss Bessie Thompson, the Chairperson of the Governors of Lea Grange School. Everyone present turned in the direction of the upright spinster lady as she rummaged in a large leather handbag before drawing out a coloured print of a beautiful tabby cat. I studied the faces of the four other people, noting the expressions of incredulity. How could she expect us all to concentrate our attention on Alice, the cat, at such a critical point of the proceedings? But this was typical of her: she was deadly serious.

On that Thursday afternoon we had assembled in my study to

interview five candidates for the position of the Second Deputy Head. The face of Hobbes-Parsons, the representative from the County Education Department, betrayed no emotion as he hardly glanced at the photograph before passing it to Muriel Carruthers, who was there to represent the parents. He was a strange fellow was Hobbes-Parsons, or Mr. Parsons, as he was known up north, where we lived and to where he had moved from the southwest. Rumour had it that he had started life in a humble working-class family as Wilf Parsons but that, after serving in the Royal Air Force, he and his twin brother had decided that the addition of a double barrel to their family name would almost guarantee advancement in their chosen careers. That the decision had been reached during a night of alcoholic indulgence did not deter them from proceeding with their scheme in which each added the name of a philosopher to his given surname. No doubt, the fact that they were both reading politics, philosophy, and economics influenced their respective choices, our colleague's brother adopting Locke-Parsons.

Apparently, when Wilfred applied for his post in our 'down-to-earth, unpretentious' county, he dropped the Hobbes just as quickly as he had picked it up at university.

"What a lovely, lovely, cuddly cat," observed Muriel Carruthers as she handed on Alice's likeness to Len Bowers, the local adviser, whom I regarded as a close friend as well as a most supportive colleague. "Too true, a beautiful animal," said Len, anything to hide his grin as he handled the photo with due reverence. The sixth member of our group, Charlie Wilson, waved away Len's attempt to pass him the picture. "I know Alice well enough. She was part of my cat's litter before I had her spayed."

Charlie was an enigma - that he was a keen cat lover was almost unbelievable. Rumour had it that, as a work-shy teenager, he had been a bookmaker's runner for several years, much to the chagrin of his splendid mother, who was a pillar of local society, treasurer of a number of charities and such like.

He was greatly affected by her sudden death and his friends tell me that, from that day on, he resolved to make something of his wasted life. His worthwhile contributions to community projects are well known throughout the Beckbridge Valley. Although he eventually became involved in politics, he never quite threw off the mantle associating him with the gaming industry. His thin black moustache, which could have been applied with a single stroke of a pencil, and his sleek, well-greased hair, parted with perfect symmetry down the centre, were utterly in keeping with his loud check suits and expensive Cuban cigars.

I liked everything about Charlie save his insistence, nay persistence, in trying to make people laugh. Completely unable to tell a joke, he either messed up the punchline or mistimed the ending. He would nevertheless collapse into fits of laughter and slap or nudge everyone who failed to join in. Usually, only he and I laughed...and I was doing it out of sympathy

Suitably flattered by the lavish praise that had been heaped upon her beloved animal, Bessie called us to order to perform the duty that was the purpose of our meeting. She could be quite forceful, when she chose. Although well into her sixties, she stood erect and straight-shouldered to a height of almost six feet. The bouffant style of her white hair, together with her high-heeled shoes, added to her imperious appearance, which was enhanced by her traditional royal blue and white garb. For this occasion, she had chosen a well-cut suit and frilly blouse.

Bessie was an enigma, generally street-wise combined with occasional lapses into naivety, in particular, in relation to the cat to which she was so devoted. Everybody thought her silly for the way she personalised the creature but we all humoured her eccentricity. For instance, having received cards from 'Bessie and Alice', for two successive Christmases, I had now taken to wording the salutations on my cards, 'To Bessie and Alice, from Adam.' However, I did have more difficulty in hiding my exasperation on the many occasions that I called at Bessie's home to drive her to a meeting.

"Do come in, Mr. Firestone, I'm not quite ready. Alice will look after you."

Then, having left me with the purring animal that insisted on walking back and forth across my shoes, depositing cat hairs on the lower regions of my well-pressed trousers, she would suddenly reappear.

"Now, now, Alice, it's no use trying to get round Mr. Firestone, he doesn't want naughty little girls like you in his school."

Yet, in spite of all this, Miss Bessie Thompson was shrewd and able, extremely strong-minded, a formidable lady. I was ever grateful for her continued support.

"Well, ladies and gentlemen, we've seen some very good people and I'm sure we can appoint a suitable deputy for Adam before we leave today."

To murmurs of "Hear, hear," the discussions began.

When the post of Second Deputy Head was originally advertised, there were several hundred enquiries eventually resulting in eighty-seven firm applications. We had stated that, in addition to the normal qualifications demanded for a senior position in a school, we were seeking to appoint someone who could develop the use of the new technology that was emerging. In particular, an essential qualification was the ability to compile a timetable for a large school.

By careful screening, the eighty-seven candidates had been reduced to five. Consequently, four men and one woman had been invited to attend but, ironically, four days before the interviews, the difficulty of maintaining a stable staff was brought home to me with a vengeance.

My telephone buzzed. "Some fellow from the Devon Education Department is on the line. Says it's urgent, must speak to you," announced my secretary.

"Put him through, please. Yes, Firestone speaking."

"Mr. Firestone, I am told that Mr. Robson is not in school today. I need to speak with him urgently. We want him to come for an interview on Thursday. I suppose you know he's applied for the headship of one of our schools?"

"Of course, I wrote his reference. It's a bit short notice, isn't it?"

"Well, yes it is. To be frank, we had him in reserve and one of the original choices has pulled out."

"Devon's a long way from Lancashire. Is it worth his while to make the journey? I mean, he being only a reserve!"

"Most definitely. Once the interviews begin, all the candidates are equal. In fact, at our last interview for a headship, the reserve got the job. As we can't get hold of him, do you mind passing on the invitation?"

Of course I didn't mind. I was delighted for Paul although I should be sorry to see him go. Two days later, he caught the overnight express from Manchester to Exeter.

Meanwhile, I pressed on with winkling out as much additional information about our applicants as I could. Some were more easily investigated than others. I encountered the most difficulty with the man who possessed the strongest support on paper. According to his written references, he was the ideal person for the job. After a few years as housemaster in a well-known boarding school, he had taken up the deputy-headship of a missionary college in Africa. Unfortunately, the tropical climate was playing havoc with his health and, because of this, he was prepared to accept a 'sideways' move to obtain a post back in England. When I telephoned the Society to follow up the written report, I was informed that no one currently working at headquarters knew him personally. Therefore, nothing could be added to what I had already been sent.

In complete contrast to this, I had a most interesting conversation with a retired headmaster living in the Cotswolds. His wife had to interrupt him pruning his roses and, as we spoke, I visualised a beautiful garden set within high walls of honey-coloured stone. From what he added to his written submission on Sarah Roberts, I had no doubt that she would be a real asset to Lea Grange. That the call lasted a full twenty minutes was due to his constant digressions on the joys of retirement, in particular, retirement in the Cotswolds. I looked forward to meeting this 'cracker of a teacher', whose career had been launched eight years earlier in my new friend's school.

Similarly, I had no trouble in pursuing my enquiries about

David James, the local candidate. He was Head of the Geography Department at my good friend Albert Crompton's school, and he came highly recommended. "He's probably the best lad I've come across, Adam," was Albert's unequivocal tribute.

"I know he's good, Albert, but can he compile a timetable?"

"I'm sure he could. I'll admit he hasn't had any practice here. I don't allow anybody to mess with my timetable. I prefer to keep it under my own control." Whilst I was musing on the adage that you couldn't teach an old dog new tricks, he continued, "You must take him, Adam. He's very, very good." I had the utmost regard for Albert Crompton, a head of some fifteen year's experience. We had become firm friends almost from the day I took up my appointment at Lea Grange. Self-opinionated, yes, stubborn, yes, tight-fisted, yes, but probably the shrewdest person that I have ever known. If David James was as good as Albert rated him, he was going to be hard to beat.

My telephone enquiries about the other two applicants, Ashley Peters and Simon Higgs, were just as encouraging if not quite so effusively delivered so, after my marathon of calls, I was extremely happy about the composition of the short list.

On the evening before the interviews, Albert Crompton's protégé, the said David James, could not settle to anything. He had intended to discuss with his wife, Mary, likely questions and suitable responses. She had been a top student in the education department of her university and she had taught for four years before the first of their two girls was born. David put great store in her knowledge and opinions.

"If we are going to have a question and answer session, love, I'd like to get started. I'm very tired and you've got a big day ahead of you."

"I just can't put my mind to it, Mary. I'm not sure I'm doing the right thing, leaving Albert. I can't imagine getting on as well with Adam Firestone. I've been thinking. I might wait till there's a vacancy for a deputy at our school."

"Look David. If you want to be a head some day, you'll have to be a deputy first."

"Agreed."

"Right then, you can't afford to hang about waiting for a job that might never materialise. If you are really worried about Adam Firestone, pop down the lane and have a word with Sue Gregory. She was practically brought up with him. She knows him as well as anyone and I'd certainly back her judgement."

Mary had known Sue ever since she and her son, Billy, had moved into their quaint little ivy-clad cottage down the lane. There was talk that Sue's husband, Billy's father that is, had been in some trouble and had left the country rather hurriedly to work in Africa. He had never shown his face in Beckbridge and the burden of rearing Billy had rested fairly and squarely on Sue's slim shoulders.

"She's done a good job with that lad," was the collective verdict of the ladies of the Women's Institute, where the friendship between Sue and Mary had begun. Although David was less acquainted with Sue, he had formed the same opinion of her. He decided to give it a try.

Fifteen minutes later, he was sitting opposite her in the neat little living kitchen. He wasted no time in coming to the point of his visit.

Sue explained, "Adam was my brother's best friend way back in our village in Yorkshire. He's eight years older than me. He was really nice in those days. I don't know him professionally but from what I've seen of him as a parent, he hasn't changed much. He's very well-liked by the other parents."

"How about Billy? How did he rate him?"

"I honestly don't know. You see, a few months before Billy left Lea Grange, Adam Firestone dealt with him very severely. I'm not sure that Billy has forgiven him, even though Adam got him a place at college."

"I remember something about Billy having an accident with a shot-gun," David ventured.

"Yes, he nearly lost an eye. The trouble with the school stemmed from then. It was awful... Anyway Billy's in the shed, why don't you ask him yourself?"

Having left Lea Grange a year earlier, Billy had completed his first year at agricultural college. I soon realised that his opinion of Adam Firestone was clear and uncomplicated. "Had you asked me a year ago, I'd have given the thumbs down. However, now I've been somewhere else for a year, I realise that Lea Grange and, yes, Adam Firestone, are a damn sight better than I gave them credit for, if you know what I mean. I wish I could have my time there over again."

"It's not unusual to feel like that about one's old school," observed David as, by discreet prompting, he moved the discussion along the lines of his enquiries. He learned a lot of valuable information about Adam Firestone, the person, and Adam Firestone, the Headmaster. It was far later than he had intended when he thanked Sue and Billy and bade them goodnight. As he walked briskly back up the dark lane, he was in a much better frame of mind. In fact he was looking forward eagerly to being appointed Second Deputy Head at Lea Grange School, or so he hoped.

Perhaps it was not too surprising that, on that same evening, another candidate was experiencing misgivings about the following day's interview. Sarah Roberts was worried about leaving the Cotswolds to move north into Lancashire.

"It's a bit late for you to be getting cold feet," growled her exasperated father.

"You'll love the people," soothed her mother, who had spent most of World War Two as an evacuee in Accrington. In those days, she was certainly safer there than in Coventry, her home town.

Sarah sighed, "It's just that the thought of Lancashire conjures up pictures of tall chimneys and cobbled streets. I'm not sure I fancy it after Cambridge and the Cotswolds."

"You're quite wrong, dear," consoled Mother. "Most of the County of Lancashire is rural. Farming is the main industry. There are very few mills left."

"It's too late to pull out now, Sarah," said Father. "Why don't you get off early in the morning and have a good look round before the interview. In any case, you might not even be offered the job."

"I certainly shall not accept it unless I'm absolutely happy about everything."

"Of course you won't, my love. Now off you go to bed and I'll get you an early breakfast," said Mother with a reassuring smile.

A bright sunny morning lifted some of Sarah's gloom, and, thanks to an early start, she spent over two hours exploring the delightful countryside bordering Beckbridge. She was pleasantly surprised by the charm of the little town. Having ear-marked a couple of attractive villages as possible areas to live, the principal cause of her apprehension about Lancashire had been removed and so, when she reported at the school for the pre-interview lunch with her rivals, she was in a very positive frame of mind.

Compared with Sarah Roberts, David had no misgivings about the area where, in fact, he had grown up. He lived within walking distance of Lea Grange, that is, if he was a good walker. It was certainly well within the range of his cycle, which he decided to employ on that lovely sunny morning. The journey was almost all downhill, so it would be a pleasant way to relax and marshal his ideas without unduly disturbing his carefully groomed appearance.

All concerned turned up on time and after the necessary introductions and pumping of hands (I couldn't help noticing that some were firmer than others), the five victims, together with the members of the interviewing committee, were seated round a large dining table in the sixth-form common room, the only suitable space big enough to accommodate us all. It was arranged so that the candidates and their inquisitors would sit alternately. I found myself between Simon Higgs and David James, with the ex-missionary teacher directly opposite.

I confess that I was slightly irritated by Simon's lack of table manners, but, I told myself, this should not impair his ability to develop modern technology, However, as the meal progressed, I became increasingly troubled by the demeanour of the man opposite. Sinister is the only word that came to mind. Whilst indulging in pleasantries, which involved laughing at Charlie Wilson's pathetic attempts at jokes, I was regretting not being more assertive in my enquiries at the missionary society.

Eventually, trepidation bordering on panic took me over. Whilst coffee was being served, I excused myself and made a beeline for my study. My call to the society received the same response as my first enquiry. "I'm awfully sorry but no-one at headquarters is actually acquainted with the gentleman." This time I would not be put off.

"Look here, I'm considering appointing this man to a very senior post in my school where he will be dealing with teenagers and their problems. There must be no question about his integrity."

"I can only refer you to the report we have sent you."

"That is not good enough. Frankly, I don't like the look of him. Is there anything I should be told? I'm holding you personally responsible. I need your name, please."

"Er…"

"May I please have your name?"

"Just a moment." A different voice came on the line.

"What number are you speaking from? Right...Yes...I've got it. Replace your receiver and I'll call back straight away."

My phone rang almost immediately. I was horrified by what I heard. In fact, the man's departure from Africa was not entirely due to ill health. Unfortunately, there had been accusations of misconduct with young boys that had never been completely proved but the college principal had suggested that it would be more appropriate for him to be employed in a day school rather than in a boarding establishment. I'd heard enough. I don't remember how the conversation ended but when I replaced the receiver, I knew that our choice had been reduced to four.

I said nothing about my call to the committee. We proceeded to interview all five candidates over the following three hours. It was whilst we were relaxing with tea and biscuits prior to choosing my new deputy that Bessie produced the photograph of her feline companion. Eventually, after an appropriate period of chitchat, our refreshment tray was removed and we directed our minds to the selection process.

Officially, the decision was the prerogative of the governors but Bessie sensibly canvassed the opinion of the professionals. We quickly agreed that the final choice would be between Sarah Roberts and David James. The other three disappointed young men were duly thanked and urged to try again before they were sent sadly back to their homes.

Bessie decided, "Let's consider Miss Roberts first." Wilf Parsons kicked off, his luke-warm approval clearly revealing that he preferred David James. Charlie Wilson thought that she had a beautiful smile and Muriel Carruthers 'simply loved' her shoes. I was grateful that Len Benson considered her to be 'very sound' because, in my opinion, she was by far the more suitable candidate for the post we had advertised.

When we moved on to discuss David James, Parsons was effusively adamant that he was the one we should appoint. "He has just given an excellent account of himself and he would be very strong when deputising for you, Mr. Firestone. Besides that, he is a county employee and it's very good for morale when we are seen to look after our own people. Surely you can't turn him down just because he stumbled a bit when you asked him how he would construct a timetable?"

While I was thinking, "More like fell flat on his face," Charlie enjoined, "That's right, Adam. We ought to be seen to be promoting local talent. Anyway, you'll be much better off with a fellow - you've already got Jean Lennox to look after the girls."

So that was it. Politics was rearing its ugly head.

I controlled my exasperation. "Mr. Parsons, it is essential that the person appointed is an expert on the curriculum and time-tabling. Whilst Mr. James has impressed us all, I am sure, I must insist that the lady is the more suitable for the job in question."

My remarks sparked off a heated discussion from which I endeavoured to remain aloof.

There was no doubt that Charlie Wilson's sexist remark had annoyed Muriel Carruthers. Meanwhile, Parsons was expending maximum effort on trying to force his opinion upon all present. Eventually, Bessie Thompson took control. "Mrs. Carruthers, gentlemen, it seems to me that we are split right down the middle so I'm going to exercise my prerogative, my casting vote."

"Good," called out Parsons, who expected that she would heed the advice of the county official. Bessie continued, "Mr. Firestone is going to have to run Lea Grange long after this meeting's over. I'm recommending that he has his choice. " Looking at me she went on, "You'd prefer Miss Roberts wouldn't you?" I tried not to look triumphant.

"Yes please, Miss Thompson." Bessie's sharp eyes flitted from Charlie Wilson to Muriel Carruthers then back again. "Mr. Wilson? Mrs. Carruthers?" Both of her fellow governors nodded their agreement and I knew that I had got the person I wanted.

A disappointed David James was invited back into my study where we all made sincere attempts to console him. Wilf Parsons promised him an interview when the next deputy headship vacancy in the county arose whilst I did my best to convince him that he had made an excellent impression.

Sarah Roberts accepted the post 'with the greatest of pleasure'. It was whilst we were toasting her success that my phone rang. My secretary spoke, "I know you were not to be disturbed but Paul Robson's on the line from Devon."

"Put him through please." An excited voice announced, "I've got the job. They've offered me the headship!"

"That's wonderful, Paul. Have you accepted?"

"Too bloody true. I say, can I tender my notice over the telephone? It's the last day of the month."

"Of course, consider it done." I turned to the committee. "Would you believe it? That was Paul Robson. He's got the headship of a school in Devon. We need another deputy. If we'd known an hour earlier, we could have had David James as well as Miss Roberts."

"Sod's law," observed whimsical Charlie, shrugging his shoulders. Len Benson was the first to react. His face lit up as he suggested, "We're all still here and David James can't have got very far." Bessie's mind was working almost as fast as Len's.

"Go and see if you can find him, Adam, and bring him back."

I caught up with him at the school gate where he had stopped to chat to our cricket coach. Back in front of the committee, still sporting cycle clips on his best pair of trousers, his smile visibly broadened as the situation was explained to him.

"I'm over the moon," was his way of signifying his acceptance of the post. Considering all the circumstances, I must confess that I was up there with him.

CHAPTER TWO

'T'aint what you do, it's the way that 'cha do it,
T'aint what you say, it's the way that 'cha say it!'

Traditional Jazz Tune.

"You've either got to be consistently severe or make out you're crazy. If they think you're unbalanced and likely to flip, they won't mess you about, Adam," he frequently used to tell me. Leonard was Head of the school where I had started my teaching career twenty years earlier. A handsome, imposing figure of a man, he had been a commander in the Royal Navy during the Second World War, captain of a destroyer escorting mine-sweepers out of Felixstowe.

To sit at Leonard's table for the midday meal was a delight. He possessed a most engaging sense of humour and his mind was a veritable store of anecdotes with which he entertained us, his fellow diners, his loyal staff. He enjoyed our unreserved allegiance and respect. He had a way of deliberately misusing words; for instance, psychiatrists were 'trick-cyclists' and our local science inspector, John Keyes, was always referred to as 'Buncher'. Think about it! Almost all of his stories were funny but, occasionally, when he described a sad incident, his obvious distress would be felt by all. I remember him being almost in tears over a young able-seaman called Lofty, who had been lost overboard in a North Sea storm. The young fresh-faced lad was wearing wellington boots at the time, affording him no chance of staying afloat long enough to be located and rescued. Leonard never ceased blaming himself for Lofty's death even though he had risked his ship for several hours by ordering a prolonged search of the raging waters.

As an officer in the Royal Navy, Leonard had dealings with all types of individuals; hence his simplistic hypothesis with regard to discipline: either be a martinet or pretend you're mad. It goes without saying that he chose the latter course, with considerable success, I'm pleased to say.

Personally, I'm the same. For me, trying to be permanently severe is too much of a strain. It causes a nasty, uncomfortable sensation in the pit of my stomach.

Of course, both of Leonard's options had a common aim, which was to deter would-be troublemakers so that they would not even dare to think about stepping out of line. However, in my experience, there's always at least one who will chance his arm against authority. It is in such a situation that my theory of instant detection is so apt: if villains are quickly apprehended, the effect on their likely imitators is miraculous.

Such was the level to which the discussion I was enjoying with my two new deputies, Sarah and David, had descended on that beautiful September evening during their second week of service at Lea Grange. Seated on comfortable reclining chairs on the western-facing verandah of the home economics flat, we had watched the setting sun disappear over the opposite end of the Beckbridge Valley as we decided upon our educational strategy for the future. Exhausted after four solid hours, I'm sure we all felt satisfied with the progress we had made. As is often the case, after we had partaken of a little of the sherry I had produced from the bottom drawer of my filing cabinet, the conversation veered towards the anecdotal.

Sarah responded positively to Leonard's hypothesis: be a brute or act mad. "Actually I agree with him. The best Head I've worked for was utterly in charge of his school by adopting an air of eternal severity. He retired a couple of years ago to a lovely cottage in the Cotswolds." I refrained from admitting that, only a few weeks earlier, I had spoken on the phone to the very fellow, as she continued, " His name was William Clarke so, predictably, he was known by the staff as W.C. When he was angry, his complexion from the neck upwards took on a bright red hue, invariably prompting the staff-room wag to remark, 'I say, W.C.'s looking a bit flushed this morning!' "

It was then David's turn to acknowledge how lucky he had

been to work for Albert Crompton who, like W.C., had a firm grip on his school although David wasn't sure whether it was by adopting fierceness or by purporting to be insane. When I suggested a combination of both, he laughed and nodded vigorously.

This gave me the cue to make my point. "Such desirable conditions don't happen automatically, you know. You've got to be able to smell trouble before it surfaces and jump on it from a great height." I recharged our glasses to protestations of "Only a drop for me, thanks," and continued with the tale.

"I was Deputy in a school where the Head had just about given up; it made life hard for everyone. Granted he was popular with the kids and the few parents who visited the school seemed to like him but he was more of a social worker than a headmaster, always willing to use the phone on their behalf. You must understand, it was quite a poor area and hardly anyone possessed a telephone. Our problems arose as soon he was required to do his proper job, especially when he should have been taking action against misbehaviour. I remembered well being called to the telephone in his absence to have my ear bent by a very angry female.

'Two of your hooligans are making my life a misery. Not content with pelting my garden shed with mud, they've taken to throwing stones at my baby's pram. I've just found two rocks on the apron. They could have killed him!'

I did my best to reassure her, 'This is dreadful. I'll deal with it at once. If I send two of my older boys to your house just before school closes, will you let them stand behind the curtains in your front room so that you can point out the culprits when they go past? I assure you, they won't trouble you again.'

'I most certainly will. I'm fed up to the teeth with your so-called students. Last year a mob ran all over my front garden and pinched half my plants.'

'Yes, well Madam, I promise you that I'll sort out your problem today but I can't help what happened a year ago, I only started at this school in September.'

'Oh, I know you're not the person I spoke to before. When I

complained to him, all he said was, ‘Running across your garden missus, is that all? You’re lucky. You should see the damage they’re doing to the school.’ ”

As my companions shook their heads in disbelief, I went on, “The two boys were identified that evening and dealt with appropriately. One of them clearly learned his lesson and never again stepped out of line, as far as I know, that is. The other? It’s a long story. In fact, Horace was never out of trouble. Although his misdemeanours were detected with monotonous regularity and punished quite severely, his irresistible inclination to offend remained with him throughout his school life and, I understand, into early manhood.

Paradoxically, his bad behaviour did not have the ripple effect that one might have expected. His peers did not respect him enough to imitate him and he was caught in the act with such regularity that he was a poor role model for any self-respecting villain. Our difficulties with him were mercifully confined to his personal misdemeanours, all too frequent, but childishly easy to uncover. However, I must say that he had one very irritating habit. When caught out and confronted with irrefutable evidence, his reaction was always the same: a truculent shrug, an insolent stare and then the statement, ‘It’s not only me!’

Horace was a sad lad with no friends, which was not surprising considering his unpleasant nature. His insistence on being a nuisance in class incurred the displeasure of his teachers, none of whom liked having him in their groups. I suspect that his parents found him obnoxious. Perhaps this was the root of the trouble. He was a big boy for his age, somewhat overweight without being gross. I’m sure that he was agile enough to climb a drainpipe if it led to something he could steal. He hated his nickname, ‘Fatso’, but could do nothing to prevent his peers using it although he was hard on smaller boys who could not out-run him. Horace had podgy cheeks and a permanent toothy grin, more of a leer, I suppose. His hair was fair, scruffy, and unkempt. I remember the time he had to stay away from school to allow it to grow again after his father had shaved his head to rid him of fleas.

He was the first pupil I got to know when I started at that school, unfortunately for the wrong reasons. A policewoman had called to return a hammer, which had the school name stamped on the handle. During the previous evening, there had been a break-in at the market-hall. The intruder, who had made off with about twenty items of clothing, had abandoned the hammer. I was left with a description of the missing articles, mainly pullovers and cardigans, and requested to assist with their recovery, should they appear on any of our pupils.

At that stage, any suspicions I may have harboured concerning Horace's likely involvement in the break-in were immediately dispelled as I stood by the entrance hall on the following morning, casting my eye over the classes as they filed in. I noted that he was wearing the usual grey sweater with the hole somewhere about navel level. However, three girls did sport new Fair Isle cardigans and several boys were wearing brand new, bright blue pullovers. They needed a little coaxing to reveal the retailer of their newly acquired wares. Apparently, they had obtained them at knockdown prices and, in view of this, their supplier had requested them to keep it a secret lest he should be inundated by requests for similar bargains. Interviewed separately, they revealed that their outfitter was Horace, whom they had not previously liked but who now seemed 'a really nice guy'.

When I confronted him with the evidence, he began by admitting half the truth. Yes, he had sold the garments but he had not stolen them: he had found them outside the market-hall on his way home from the cinema. Gentle interrogation established two vital points: the market-hall was nowhere near his route home from the cinema and he did not know the name of the film currently showing. My undertaking to ask the police to give him a chance finally persuaded him to admit his guilt, not without asserting, 'It weren't only me.' As he had not previously been in trouble with the law, he got away with a caution. I resolved to keep an eye on him, to foster a relationship, which might even develop into mutual trust. A golden opportunity soon presented itself.

At the time, an old aunt of mine was living in a tied cottage on land owned by the Duke of Norfolk, with whom she had been in service in her younger days. One Saturday morning, I was motoring slowly along the driveway to her little house when, in the distance by the boundary wall, I recognised Horace, who was grubbing in the undergrowth and placing his discoveries in a small tin. When I called across to ask him what he was doing, he made no attempt to hide his activities. On the contrary he cheerfully trotted over to me and, through the passenger side window, which my wife had wound down, he proudly thrust a rusty old baked-beans can, which was half full of wriggling worms. After he had withdrawn his prize and only when the pandemonium his gesture had created had subsided, he informed me that he regularly went to that place to collect worms for his Sunday fishing excursions. Was this the opportunity I had been looking for to forge a friendship with this unpleasant lad? Ought I to take up angling, only on an occasional basis, of course?

Alas, before I had even decided on the equipment I should need, let alone purchase anything, he was in trouble again. On that occasion, no sophisticated detective was required. Our anti-hero had broken into and entered a local brewery. Instead of seeking out where the cash was held, Horace had decided to sample the various bottled beers, a pursuit which inevitably had induced the drunken stupor in which he was discovered by the first drayman to arrive at work the following morning. This time, there was nothing I could do to prevent a court appearance even if I had tried, which I didn't. The magistrates ignored his plea of, 'It weren't only me', and he received a period of probation. His formal relationship with the judicial authorities had commenced!"

David enquired, "Did you buy a fishing rod?"

"I hadn't got round to it before our Horace struck again, this time causing me a great deal of trouble and anxiety. The episode began on the second morning of a new school year. I had changed my teaching base, having moved into the only form room in the school that had a secure stock cupboard. Consequently, it was where any valuable items were locked away overnight. Before school started on that morning, my two trusted monitors breathlessly informed me that six sets of geometrical drawing instruments, out of a batch of thirty, had been 'nicked'. The situation was particularly embarrassing because the previous occupant of that form-room had somehow managed keep everything safe and sound. Yet here I was, next in line of authority to the Head, and my security had been breached within a matter of twenty-four hours!

This was the line I adopted with the class of sixteen-year old boys, my tutor group, who were seated in front of me at morning registration. I stressed my wretched position, in particular how some members of the staff may laugh at my predicament behind my back and henceforth regard me as unworthy of my exalted position.

My pleas did not fall upon deaf ears. Loyalty prevailed! Suddenly, the smallest boy in the group, staring resolutely ahead, announced, 'Fatso's had them.' The silence was as menacing as the looks that my faithful band turned on Horace, whose crimson complexion and panic-stricken countenance ruled out any possibility of his pleading either innocence or ignorance. My question, 'Is this true?' was answered by an almost imperceptible nod of his guilty head, a sort of a shudder. He was more afraid of the wrath of his peers than either of me or of the punishment that an offender already on probation would be likely to receive.

My interrogation continued with vigour, allowing him no time to fabricate either lies or excuses. 'Where are they now?' He gave me a surly stare but did not answer my question. Perhaps the disgust and hostility emanating from all around him caused this loss of speech. Whilst there were many rogues among his fellow students, there was a primitive code of honour: basically, you don't mess on your own doorstep. Secure in the knowledge that there would be no retribution whilst the rest of the group displayed such anger towards the fat one, my diminutive informant again broke the silence.

'He sold them to Eliza Jane.'

The said recipient was the proprietress of the local pawnshop, a brisk business lady, who never asked awkward questions. I looked round the class, and I chose the boy whose glare in Horace's direction displayed the most ferocity.

'John, will you please escort this misguided person to Eliza Jane's and tell her that she has acquired some items that were stolen from school. Explain that if she gives back the sets straight away, we shall not take any further action. If she keeps the goods, she'll be reported to the police for handling stolen property.'

'It'll be a pleasure, Sir.' As he slowly got to his feet, Horace plucked up enough courage to croak,

'It's not only me who's been in t'stock room.' Ignoring his plea as being unworthy of a reply, I pointed firmly to the door and, to a chorus of hisses, he half ran from the room, closely policed by his formidable six-foot tall mentor.

Apparently, Eliza Jane almost fell over herself to give the stolen goods back to John, assuring him that she had been completely deceived by Horace. Relieved to have recovered all six sets, I let the matter rest. To involve the police would merely have added to the school's bad reputation. So the wretched thief escaped with the punishment that I metered out to him, after his father had been consulted, of course.

During his few remaining months at school, he managed to stay out of trouble or, more to the point, to avoid detection. I next heard of him about three years later. He had been taken on by the captain of a trawler sailing from Grimsby to fish in Icelandic waters. By all accounts, he was soon about as unpopular with his shipmates as he had been with his fellow students at school and, in view of this, he should have been far more careful when the ship returned to port. On the contrary, he rushed headlong into a celebratory drinking session, eventually sobering up to discover that his wallet was completely empty.

The last time I heard anything of Horace was three or four years later through the columns of a local evening paper. The headline, 'Man jailed for affray' was followed by a brief account of the incident in which my ex-pupil figured all too prominently. However, it was the conclusion of the report that particularly caught my attention: 'When asked if the defendant had anything to say before sentence was passed, his advocate stated that his client had instructed him to inform the Court that there were other persons involved in addition to himself.' I suppose that this can be roughly translated to mean, 'It weren't only me!' "

CHAPTER THREE

'It is a capital mistake to theorise before one has data.'

Sherlock Holmes - Sir Arthur Conan Doyle.

"Headmaster, did Roy the Boy leave a forwarding address when he 'scarpered'?" Engrossed as I was in a mountain of monthly returns, I was in no mood to appreciate Roger Hansard's caustic wit. I glowered at the figure of my music master, languishing in my study doorway.

"You're joking, of course! Anyway, why should you want to contact him? I thought he was the bane of your life."

"It's not him I want to see, it's that damned trombone. He's pinched it!"

"Which damned trombone? Not...not that trombone? Oh no! How can you be sure?"

"Quite easily, Headmaster. In the first place, it's missing. In the second place, he told Jack the Lad he was going to London to join a band."

My exasperation boiled over. "Join a bloody band - he's only been learning for three weeks! You should never have let him have a new instrument."

Roger flushed, stammered, and almost suffered an apoplectic fit. " I... I" he emphasised the word, "I should not have let him have it? With respect, Headmaster, it was you who suggested lending him a trombone. 'Show him we trust him', you said."

I didn't need Roger to remind me of my involvement, especially in the superciliously triumphant manner he was wont to adopt in such circumstances. I could not deny that Roger had been anything but keen when Roy had applied to join the brass band so that he could learn the trombone. It was indeed I who had persuaded him to accept the youngster on the grounds that it would provide him with a purpose in life and perhaps encourage him to get into a little less trouble.

"Lend him that old euphonium to begin with," I had suggested. "Promise him a trombone when he can play a scale. That will keep him quiet for a few weeks."

"Which it definitely did not," was Roger's quick response. "He soon called our bluff, didn't he? He learned a scale in three days and he was playing 'Three Blind Mice' after a fortnight." Roy's commendable progress certainly had created a problem for us. Bluntly stated, we had no spare trombone to issue to him. Nevertheless, I was determined to keep our side of the bargain. Roy already had very little trust or regard for authority, which he considered as interfering too much in his young life. If we were to build on the foundations that becoming a member of that elite body, the school brass band, would provide, we must keep our promise and produce a trombone from somewhere.

Roy the Boy had acquired his nickname through the outrageous antics he got up to, both in and out of school. The Artful Dodger would have been an even more appropriate pseudonym but that title had been famously bestowed over a century earlier. Actually, he was quite likeable, mischievous rather than villainous. In recent times, life had been hard on him. His father had deserted the family and his mother had suffered a breakdown. This misfortune had condemned her to a prolonged stay in hospital and Roy to a placement in a children's home near to Lea Grange. So about a year ago, we had welcomed him into the fold and just when we were beginning to detect some progress with this difficult lad, he had departed. I was furious that he had taken the trombone, especially because I had risked my reputation to acquire it. Finding myself without the necessary finances to purchase an instrument, I'd resorted to somewhat questionable, certainly unconventional, methods. Normally, I should have tapped the obvious source of ready cash, the unofficial school fund, but the balance was dangerously low mainly because the music department had already been dipping into it as if there were no tomorrow. To allocate any more to music would both insult and enrage the other worthy claimants. They had deferred to Roger Hansard's instrumental demands on too many occasions in the past.

In making this observation, I am in no way intending to criticise Roger, Indeed, his wonderful work in extending the influence of music throughout the school, developing the choir, the orchestra and the brass band, had received my whole-hearted admiration and support. With over eighty students learning instruments, Lea Grange had rightly earned its reputation as a beacon of musical excellence, a plaudit that was not lightly conferred in the Beckbridge Valley, famous for its choral and instrumental achievements.

It was unfortunate that Roger and Wilfred Parsons, the school's adviser, did not see eye to eye on musical education. Roger, ever the traditionalist, had no time for the modern approach, 'tinkering with piffling little class-room instruments' such as xylophones, kettledrums and tambourines. At the other extreme, Parsons would never acknowledge the success of Roger's formal approach, although he always knocked on our door when he needed a band to play for a special occasion. Personally, I could never understand why both methods could not be employed side by side but Roger assured me that 'playing with toys' would undermine the kids' desire to learn to play 'properly'.

Ever since I joined the teaching profession, I have believed that a school with a good record in sport combined with a good tradition in music is bound to be successful. Therefore, I was ever grateful to Roger Hansard for his excellent work. His cavalier attitude did cause me embarrassment at times but it provided me with amusement more often than not. I well remember an occasion when he and I were cajoled by Parsons to join a group on a visit to York University, where the Department of Music was pioneering a new approach to the subject. With the commendable aim of fostering an appreciation of their beloved subject in all pupils, various avant-garde techniques were demonstrated. One memorable session was devoted to a film depicting a bearded young master, resplendent in bracelet and necklace, encouraging his young charges to 'get a feel' of the instruments that were strewn about the classroom.

"If any of our kids touched my piano, I'd tan their back-sides," was Roger's way of indicating to me, in a low whisper I'm relieved to say, that he was not favourably impressed. That incident and Roger's excitement every time we passed over the numerous level crossings found in East Yorkshire are my two most profound memories of that day. I should explain that Roger Hansard's love of music is only rivalled by his obsession for railway trains.

To return to the business in hand, that is, the acquisition of a trombone for Roy the Boy, my only other option was to raid the capitation allowance: the money provided by the Local Authority with which to purchase all our requirements in books, materials, and equipment. On the face of it, this presented me with an insurmountable problem: the bureaucrats of County Hall operated on the unwavering conviction that it is he who pays the piper who calls the tune. Accordingly, although schools were ostensibly free to spend their allowances as they deemed appropriate, there was an over-riding proviso. All items costing over £100 had to be vetted by an adviser on the grounds that, wherever possible, the benefits of the allowance should be enjoyed by all pupils rather than by an elite few. As a trombone would cost about double the arbitrarily determined figure, my order was bound to be placed in front of, and automatically rejected by, our friendly adviser.

Wilfred Parsons was constantly preaching that capitation allowances must not be used to purchase large items intended for the use of an individual. In general, I had no quarrel with this point of view but Roy's case was different! I would have to find a way to hoodwink the bureaucrats and thereby prevent Parsons from getting involved.

I was confident that I could out-think the pen pushers of the accounts department. Two years earlier, I had bamboozled much bigger fish. It was when the school buildings were being extended and we were submitting orders to furnish the newly built rooms, a straightforward task, one would imagine. Not so, for in a comfortable chair at County Hall sat a middle manager, whose sole function was to peruse the invoices, pruning from each one a few chairs, the odd table and a cupboard or two. Having been alerted to this likely desecration of my orders by my fellow Headmaster, Albert Crompton, who recently had been on the receiving end of the process, I took evasive action. Approximately halfway down the list of rooms for which I claimed furniture, I inserted an additional but fictitious room, in the hope that it would be overlooked. It was designated 'Audio-visual' and it was tucked in between 'Geography' and 'Chemistry'. Two weeks later, when my pruned requests were returned to me, I noted with triumph that the items approved to furnish the non-existent room more than compensated for those, which had been removed from the list of bona fide rooms by the bureaucrat's blue pencil.

I decided to adopt similar tactics to obtain the trombone. "Roger, phone your supplier and arrange to collect the instrument. Warn him that the official invoice will arrive in four parts, each on a different day." I then wrote four separate orders for each of the following items: Trombone slide, Trombone horn, Trombone mouthpiece, Trombone case. As each one was priced at less than £100, they all passed through without delay.

So Roy the Boy got his beautiful brand new trombone and, less than three weeks later, the cad absconded with it.

"To think we went to all that trouble for that little devil! He's not going to get away with it, Roger. Let me think about it; I'll get back to you." The detective in me took over. The monthly returns temporarily forgotten, I concentrated my whole attention on tracking Roy and thereby recovering the trombone. Sherlock Holmes always began by eliminating the impossible on the grounds that whatever remained must be the truth. I decided to start by examining the known facts in the hope that they would lead me to the unknown, that is, to the whereabouts of Roy and the trombone.

My first positive step was a telephone call to Richard, the warden of the diagnostic centre, which had doubled as Roy's home for the past year. If anyone could help me, he would. Richard was among the very small circle of persons whom Roy liked and trusted. He had the perfect disposition for his demanding job, sensitive and caring towards his charges, exuding the warmth and security so essential for youngsters deprived of the normal parental set-up. Apparently the lad always contrived to sit by his surrogate dad at the evening meal and he was Richard's chief unpaid assistant in his dealings with the younger members of the centre. I was banking on my friend and I was not disappointed. His first words went some way towards lessening my anxieties.

"Run away to London to join a band! That's absolute nonsense, Adam. He's having you on. No, he's gone back home." This was sweet music in my ears.

"Do you have an address?"

"Well, strictly speaking, he hasn't gone back to his own home. He's gone to stay with his grandma for a few days so his mother can get their house in order. She's been in hospital for a long time."

"Yes, I know that, Richard." I was trying to hide my impatience. "Have you got his granny's address? Is she on the phone?"

"Yes and no; I know her address but she isn't on the phone."

An hour or so later, when Roger Hansard answered my summons, I was peering through a magnifying glass at the A to Z of Manchester. I located a street in an area known as Blackley, a foreign land as far as I was concerned.

"I've asked David James to cover your teaching groups this afternoon. We are off to visit the metropolis!"

It was a little after three when Roger manoeuvred his Rover 18 into the street that I had circled on the map. Our quest had been anything but straightforward on an unusually hot afternoon and our normal good humour was beginning to fray at the edges. My out-of-date A to Z had not warned of the unbelievable number of new roads under construction, let alone the numerous diversions that were a natural consequence. I didn't attempt to count the rows of terraced houses that were being knocked down in the name of improved communications. It resembled a bomb site decorated with new green and white signs indicating the way to such places as Stockport, Sheffield and Manchester Airport, with no reference whatsoever to Granny's humble street. Over the whole district hung a grey pallor of acrid smoke, rising from the multitude of smouldering fires slowly burning away the rotting floorboards and joists of the demolished properties.

My chauffeur addressed me. "I'll pull in here, opposite number twelve, then we can sidle up to the house and catch him unawares." This was sensible considering the size of Roger's limousine compared to the rusting old bangers that littered the desolate street.

"Good thinking, Roger."

By now a posse of scruffy looking lads, who had appeared from nowhere, were admiring the gleaming vehicle, prompting my companion to suggest, "Can you manage on your own? I'd rather stay and guard my car, if you don't mind."

As I stepped on to the pavement, I overheard one of the urchins say, "It's the rozzers lads, time to make ourselves scarce!" Their departure was even quicker than their original appearance.

A passage between two terraced blocks led to the rear of number forty-two, a shared yard with a pigeon loft at one end and a couple of rabbit hutches at the other. A lady with an Irish accent informed me that Roy's granny had moved to live with her son near Bolton. She went on to tell me, "The whole street's condemned to come down next month, Sir. Me and my lad here are on a short-term lease from the Council." As I regarded the little lady and her strapping son, who had moved into a protective position behind her, I remember thinking that the poor old girl's choice of residence had been somewhat limited: it was on the only street within half a mile that was still standing!

I asked my informant, "I don't suppose you've any idea of her new address?"

The lad visibly stiffened and automatically clenched his fists whilst she immediately became less helpful. I think they took me for a debt collector. It was the son who demanded, "Who are you? What do you want with her?"

As soon as I had satisfied them of my true identity, she resumed her affable approach. In fact, she did know the new address, left with her by Granny so that she could re-direct any mail. "Not that there have been any letters to send on," she said rummaging among her official papers which were stored in an old biscuit tin. "Here it is!" I thanked her and returned to break the news of our wild-goose chase to Roger. He considered the address.

"Turton: a nice little place. Not too big. We should be able to find the house quite easily. I think we should go straight away," was Roger's enthusiastic offering. I was just as keen to recover the trombone so I readily agreed, although I was beginning to wonder how on earth the Headmaster of a large school, accompanied by his Director of Music, could justify chasing around the outskirts of a large city in pursuit of one boy and his instrument. I quickly reconciled myself: if we don't deal promptly with dastardly behaviour, others will be sure to chance their luck, sooner or later.

We found the new residence easily enough. Situated on the outskirts of a picturesque village in the foothills of the Pennines, it stood at the end of a row of small detached houses. What a contrast from the semi-slum we had stood outside less than an hour earlier: privet hedges, rose bushes, well-kept crazy pathways...peace and tranquillity all around. I was pleased for Roy. It was certainly in a superior district. That said we were not prepared for the shock that was awaiting us. Following our unsuccessful attempts to elicit a response from inside, our loud banging disturbed the neighbours sufficiently to bring out a white-haired gentleman from the house next door. Yes, we had come to the right place. No, there would be nobody in until about seven, the time that Roy's uncle normally returned from Bury. He had a bric-a-brac stall on the market: pots and pans, small tables, all sorts of things. The dreaded thought came to Roger and me at the same moment!

"Does he sell musical instruments?"

"Probably. As I told you, he sells anything."

In no time at all, we were seeking a parking meter adjacent to Bury market. The stall was near the entrance and by the time we had drawn level with it, I had already scanned it twice in case a gleaming trombone was among the articles for sale. From the rear of the stall, Roy saw us first. Remarkably, he was not at all perturbed by our presence.

"Hello, Sirs." He stressed the Hello. "This is my Uncle Stan."

As calmly as possible, I asked Roy what had happened to the

trombone. He gave me an incredulous stare.

"Oh, you think I've pinched it! Oh no, Sir. I swapped it with Tommy Dorsey."

Roger intervened for my benefit, "He means Tommy Dawkins: the boy who played 'Acrobat' at the last concert. His nickname's Tommy Dorsey, after a famous trombonist of the Forties."

I hope my impatience did not offend him. "Yes, yes. As it happens, I was brought up in the 'swing' era, Benny Goodman, Glen Miller and all that...and I do know my own students, thank you, Mr. Hansard." Turning to Roy, I enquired, "Why did you give it to Tommy, whatever his name is, instead of Mr. Hansard?"

"Because he told me that he was to have it. He gave me his old one to hand in. Tommy's the top man in the band; I dare not argue with him. In any case, I thought you knew about it, Mr. Hansard." I fixed Roy with my most menacing stare. "Are you speaking the truth, lad?"

Roger came quickly to his defence. "I think he is, Headmaster. An old trombone case did appear in the music storeroom at the end of last week. I kept meaning to have a look to see what's inside it, after I'd sorted out this problem, of course."

"It seems that we've wasted a whole day sorting out two problems when there would not even have been one if only you had kept a keener eye on what people chuck into your stock room!" I sighed with an air of resignation.

CHAPTER FOUR

'Ev'ry member of the force
Has a watch and chain, of course;
If you want to know the time,
Ask a Policeman!'

E. W. Rogers.

"Call me Bobby - everybody else does."

Detective Constable Hubert Charlton was seated opposite me, soaking in the warmth of the living fire, which permeated my comfortable study. In my younger days, all policemen were 'Bobbies' so I presumed that the nickname he was proffering was more likely connected with England's illustrious centre forward than with Sir Robert Peel, the founder of the police force. Having said that, the appearance of my visitor bore no resemblance whatsoever to that of the famous footballer.

In actual fact, he was blessed with thick, black curly hair crowning a ruddy complexion from which piercing blue eyes left one in no doubt that their owner was taking very careful note of his surroundings - both human and inanimate. I would not have taken him for a policeman. In his speckled brown Harris tweed jacket, fawn corduroy slacks, polished brown brogues and woollen checked shirt with knitted tie, he was more like a game-keeper - not shabby but certainly not a snappy dresser. He would pass unnoticed in a crowd, which I assumed was his basic intention. I should imagine that his height only just attained the level required for entry to the force but his loose-fitting jacket could not conceal his powerful build.

He had telephoned earlier that day to arrange a meeting about a 'couple of matters of mutual interest'. Half past four had been agreed and my thoughtful secretary had provided us with a tray of tea and chocolate biscuits. Remarking that he could easily adapt to 'this kind of life', he went on to explain that he had been transferred to the local force only recently from a 'desk job' in County Headquarters and that he was keen to make a name for himself. He had been redeployed as cover for Sergeant Abbott, who had been obliged to take a spell of sick leave.

"I'll tell you about 'Bud' Abbott in a minute. First of all, I must give you the good news about two of your pupils." Whilst I was considering whether it was obligatory for all policemen to adopt pseudonyms based on the names of famous people, he continued, "I suppose you know Chris Davidson and David Rimmer. We're very grateful to them. They showed a lot of initiative." He shook his head with disbelief and chuckled. "The smart guys helped us to recover a vehicle that had been missing for weeks."

"Tell me more." I was always pleased to accept compliments on behalf of the school.

The agreeable narrative continued, "Well, it appears that they came across a van a few days ago, parked quite innocently on a side road leading to the recreation ground. As it seemed to them to be in exactly the same place when they passed it on the following day, they 'borrowed' a piece of chalk from your art room and made a mark at the bottom of the two nearside tyres where they touched the pavement, if you get my meaning."

I nodded eagerly as he proceeded. "The lads then checked their handiwork on the following day and, concluding that the van had still not been moved, they noted its number plate and called in at the station. To their joy and the duty officer's amazement, it transpired to be the number of a stolen vehicle. The Chief Inspector is delighted and he has sent both boys a letter of appreciation."

"I'll make a point of using this in one of my assemblies next week and, of course, I'll give them a pat on the back myself."

"Well Mr. Firestone, it's their initiative that has encouraged me to come and see you. But first, a word about poor old 'Bud' Abbott. I believe you know him." I suppressed a frown.

"Yes, we served together on a Save the Children fund-raising committee last year. We were quite good friends but we haven't been in contact since the finger-printing fiasco."

'Bobby' took over. "That's what I'm here to discuss with you. Bud has insisted that I apologise to you on his behalf for what he says was a rude outburst. He's not well, you know." In actual fact, I did not know and, frankly, I didn't give a damn either about Colin 'Bud' Abbott or about his sick leave. I cannot recall a situation where a so-called responsible person has behaved with such a lack of control as the sergeant had displayed only a few weeks earlier. Until I answered that fateful telephone call, we had been more than fellow fund-raisers - I had looked upon him as a close friend. That's why his violent reaction came as such a surprise.

It all began when a very distressed mum pleaded to see me urgently. Her twelve-year-old son had been to a matinée at the local cinema on the previous Saturday, accompanied by a couple of older boys who lived close by. Apparently, one of the older lads had gone into Woolworth's to buy a Mars Bar. As the other two had spent up, they stayed outside, window-shopping. Suddenly, they were aware of a disturbance, which turned out to be a scuffle between their friend and a shop assistant, who had caught him stealing the Mars Bar instead of paying for it.

A policeman was summoned and he escorted all three to the station. Their parents were sent for and Sergeant Abbott immediately tore into them, going on at length about parental responsibility and such like. The light-fingered one escaped with a caution on the understanding that his parents agreed to his fingerprints being taken. The sergeant then attempted to cajole the parents of the other two into allowing the police to take their prints. When they flatly refused, he gave them forty-eight hours to think again, threatening that he might be obliged to 'take the matter further'.

The distraught mother who stood before me on the following Monday morning had come to seek my advice. By asking me if the sergeant's threat was a legitimate one, she placed me in an invidious position. Of course he could not force her to allow her son to be fingerprinted and I lost no time in telling her so. "Just say 'No' and stick to your guns." I suppose that I did not expect her to quote me to the sergeant as the authority for her decision, so when my telephone exploded, I was somewhat taken aback.

My erstwhile friend stopped short of swearing but only just. In a tirade of insulting language, he left me in no doubt of what he thought of me personally, of how he rated my ability as a headmaster, and, finally, his opinion of my suitability to be a magistrate. I was neither fit to preside over the education of young people nor to sit in judgement of my peers. Any attempt to reason with him would have fallen on deaf ears. In fact, I had not had the chance to utter a single word when he slammed the phone back into its cradle.

I realised that Detective Constable Charlton was still speaking. "As I was saying, he's not well. Actually, he could be in serious trouble. Disciplinary proceedings are on the cards and all because he's too keen. That's why he was furious when you thwarted his attempt to fingerprint your pupil. He has a wild ambition to compile a dossier of the prints of every person in the Beckbridge Valley."

"He must be mentally unbalanced to even attempt such a massive undertaking."

"It's not for me to comment on the sanity of my superiors. Suffice it to say that he's been seconded on full pay whilst his assault is investigated."

The situation was deteriorating rapidly. "His assault?" I stammered.

"Oh yes, you won't have heard about it yet. It's not been released to the papers."

My curiosity got the better of me. "Now you've whetted my appetite, you'll have to tell me the full story. Perhaps it will go some way to explain his verbal assault on me."

My visitor fixed me with a steady gaze for quite a while without replying. I think he felt that he had already said too much. I tried a little gentle persuasion. "Come on, Officer, we are both professionals working together for the common good."

He relented, "I suppose there's no harm in telling you. The news will be all over the Valley in a day or two." Detective Constable Charlton then proceeded with a most bizarre account of how Sergeant Abbott had landed himself into a dreadful mess.

Two days earlier, round about midnight, a young uniformed officer had encountered three drunks who were creating a disturbance in the town square watched by a crowd of a dozen or so onlookers. When they were told to 'move along and get off home', they meekly obeyed and all was soon peaceful once again.

However, about thirty minutes later, the young policeman again came across them, on this occasion down a deserted side street. They had attracted his attention by shouting obscenities and by hammering on shop doors.

The constable decided that their behaviour had got worse rather than better since he had first spoken to them so, before approaching them a second time, he reported the situation to the station on his short-wave radio. It was as well that he did because when they became aware of his approach, they stopped hammering and concentrated their abuse on him. Although they did not actually touch him, they were very threatening. He had to move smartly backwards to prevent one of them spitting on his boots.

At that moment an unmarked police car turned into the alley at a high speed and pulled up with a screeching of brakes. Out jumped Sergeant Abbott, in plain clothes, of course. When he attempted to intervene, the drunks treated him to a mouthful of unprintable obscenities inviting him to leave the scene forthwith and to mind his own business. He turned to his young colleague: "Give me your stick, son!" Here I should explain that 'stick' is a police term for a truncheon.

"Your stick, lad," he repeated, right arm outstretched towards his subordinate. With a single sweeping movement, he struck all three troublemakers across their heads: not a difficult operation considering how severely their mobility had been impaired by the amount of alcohol they had consumed. Then, as they stood transfixed with horror, he set about beating each in turn across the head and shoulders until he eventually had to stop for breath.

The young policeman had only recently completed his initial training and the 'do's' and 'don'ts' with which he had been indoctrinated at college were ringing loudly in his ears. Bemused and horrified at what was happening in front of his very eyes, he grasped the opportunity offered by the brief pause and smartly secured his sergeant in an arm lock. As he was pleading, "That's enough, Sergeant! They've had enough!" a patrol car, itself answering the earlier call, arrived on the scene. The youths were rushed to hospital, where one was found to be seriously hurt, and Sergeant Abbott was summarily relieved of his duties. At the time of telling, he was undergoing psychological tests to assess his fitness for the job. Much worse, the authorities had no alternative but to charge him with common assault, perhaps even Grievous Bodily Harm.

"I understand now what you meant about him being too keen," I said.

"Yes, it's a shame really because his intentions were so good. He wanted to convert the Beckbridge Valley into a crime-free area."

"I'd subscribe to that if it were humanly possible."

"That's the main reason that I've come to see you, Mr. Firestone. I want to carry on with the sergeant's good work and I believe you can help, if you will."

At this suggestion, I admit to experiencing a slight shiver down my spine. Since I was a small boy, I have dreamed of being a detective! Was this to be my chance, albeit somewhat belatedly? "How do you mean? How can I possibly help? You'll have to be more explicit." With an appropriate display of modesty, I placed stress on the 'I'.

The officer warmed to his theme. "Let us begin with your two lads who discovered the stolen van. They used their eyes and they used their brains. If we can encourage all, or even the majority, of your pupils to do the same, we can prevent a lot of crime by stamping on it before it has had time to develop. The certainty of being caught is the best deterrent in existence."

"Stop it before it even raises its ugly head!" I echoed. "That's my philosophy for Lea Grange...and I can tell you, it works very well."

"I've come to the right place then. You're a man after my own heart." He went on, "Tell me, Mr. Firestone, how do you manage to keep one step ahead of the little beggars?"

"I've never really thought about strategies. I was a bit of a handful myself, when I was a boy at school. 'His efforts don't exhaust him' was a typical comment by my own Headmaster on my annual report. Then again, I've mixed with some rum characters in my time."

"I suppose you picked up how they think, these people who walk a tight-rope with the law."

"Something like that, Bobby. In the 1940s, when I was in a youth club, I had a roguish friend called Vincent. He played a piano accordion and I used to accompany him on an old set of drums. In fact, it is Vincent whom I have to thank for introducing me to traditional jazz. His favourite number was 'Bye bye blues' and I liked it because it enabled me to perform a few drum breaks. Fortunately, jazz was the only thing I allowed him to introduce me to.

"It was during the Second World War and, eventually, we both enlisted in the Royal Air Force. After undergoing our initial training at separate venues, our paths crossed when we were sent to the same camp in Essex to await a permanent posting. During a night of celebrating our reunion, Vincent confided to me that he had hit upon a foolproof method of obtaining subsidised travel on the railway. In those days, train tickets were made of thin cardboard; about two inches by one in size, and perforated down the middle. At the end of one's outward journey, the ticket collector would tear off one half of the ticket, leaving the other half to be used on the return journey. Vincent realised that, if he could somehow retain this half ticket at the end of his return journey, he would be able to use it time and time again, provided that he could avoid it being clipped to pieces by the ticket collector every time he entered a railway station.

"At the time, he was living in Sheffield and every Friday night he would hitch-hike home from Essex and return to base on Sunday. To preserve his precious return half and avoid having it clipped, Vincent negotiated his way on to Sheffield station by purchasing, for a few pence, a ticket to Chesterfield, which was the first stop down the line. Once on the train, he could use his return half if an inspector asked to see it. On his arrival in London, he crossed over to the station for Essex and bought a single ticket, again relatively cheaply, to the camp, thus retaining his return half for use the following weekend."

"I shouldn't imagine that any of the kids in your school are as devious as Vincent."

"Well, I sincerely hope not especially as when I bumped into him years later, he was still up to no good. He had developed a window-cleaning business, 'Commercial properties, Adam, Oh no, definitely not houses. You see, with houses, you have to clean them; otherwise the old biddies won't pay. With factories and offices you only need to clean the windows at the front of the building. You just give the rest a quick wipe over.'

"Yes Bobby, when you've rubbed shoulders with someone like Vincent, petty crimes by school kids are not too difficult to spot. Having said that, I'm not sure that my policy of jumping on trouble almost before it happens can be translated to the wider community."

My visitor would not be put off. "I think we can do it if we work together. Here is what I have in mind."

Leaning forward enthusiastically and using his hands to emphasise certain words, he launched himself into a series of suggestions on how we, the members of Lea Grange School, could make a significant contribution to the fight against crime in our neighbourhood. Starting from the general point that there will always be people committing crimes, often in front of our eyes, he was sure that we could all be taught to recognise the telltale signs that would give them away. Of course, he would not want us to place ourselves in danger by tackling law-breakers but he hoped that, if we learned to use our senses in a positive way, we could provide invaluable assistance to our police force.

In answer to my protest that under no circumstances would I encourage our youngsters to spy on their neighbours, he asked me to consider the following two alternatives: on seeing a thief steal a friend's bicycle, would I remain silent and let it happen or would I take sensible steps to either deter the thief or get him caught? I did not interrupt him again.

He requested permission to arrange for crime-prevention lectures to be incorporated into our curriculum. Apparently, they are not only extremely entertaining, they are very challenging and packed with useful tips such as the ploy our two celebrated pupils had used in the case of the stolen motor vehicle.

By the time he departed that evening, I had agreed to consider a programme of talks for use in our General Studies periods and he had agreed to my suggestion that he should come back soon to discuss the dangers of allowing one's enthusiasm to apprehend criminals to override one's good sense. My request was prompted by a salutary experience that had happened to me only a few months earlier. I had seen how a promising young detective had allowed eagerness to prevail over discretion, with embarrassing consequences that would do no good whatsoever for his promotion prospects. True, he had not fallen as far as poor old 'Bud' Abbot but there was a lesson to be learned from the story. I promised to tell it to 'Bobby' Charlton at our next meeting.

CHAPTER FIVE

'Motivation is concerned with the dynamic element in human nature.
It is the driving power behind behaviour.'

Charles Wilfrid Valentine.

When Detective Constable 'Bobby' Charlton next called in to see me, I hardly recognised him as the clean-shaven, fresh-faced, tidily dressed young man I had met for the first time, only a week earlier. The officer seated opposite me wore a pair of blue overalls half hidden by a dirty anorak and his chin could not have felt the effect of a razor for at least three days. On the floor under his chair, I could just see a square green tin; the kind workmen use to carry their midday sandwiches.

In answer to my quizzical expression, he explained the reason for the dramatic change in his appearance.

"I'm on observation in the Lake District. Over the past month, there's been a spate of burglaries there and we have a good idea who's responsible."

The Lake District to which he was referring was not the famous National Park in Cumbria. It was a leafy district of Beckbridge, where most of the expensive properties were located, so called because the roads had been named after the towns and villages of that beautiful area of the Northwest. Windermere Crescent, Ambleside Avenue, and Coniston Close were typical addresses. He went on,

"It's a sophisticated criminal operation, fronted by two window cleaners whose accents aren't from round here. We think that they note when people are away and then either they or their accomplices come back and burgle the deserted homes. The sooner that all the families in the big towns near here get their own record-players, the better."

"How do you mean?"

"Perhaps they'll stop coming over to Beckbridge to pinch ours!"

I smiled with him at his cynical joke, which I expect he had cracked on numerous occasions. I wished him and his colleagues' good fortune in their operation before I moved on to the main reason for our meeting. I had taken quite a liking to my enthusiastic young friend and I intended to give him a timely warning about letting keenness for success obliterate his sense of propriety.

Before I could begin, he went on, "The annoying thing is that these new mobile radios have a mind of their own. They'll only transmit from where they think fit. Heaven help us if we ever need to summon assistance in a hurry. This little devil of mine won't work in Bedale Road. If I need to call the station in a hurry from the Lake District, I have to leg it to the top of Coniston Close."

"That's a very steep climb. Something must be blocking your signal lower down," I offered. "At least you know where to run when you want to send a message!"

He was not amused so I tried again. "You are not the first policeman who has had to switch roads quickly in the line of duty. There was once a young copper in Sheffield who came across a dead dog in Fitzalan Square. As soon as he started to compile a report he realised that he couldn't spell 'Fitzalan' so, without a moment's hesitation, he picked up the unfortunate creature and carried it the few yards into Angel Street."

He shook his head and looked impassive. He was still not amused. I don't think he liked my anecdote; I'm sure he did not believe it.

"Anyway, Bobby, last week, I promised to tell you the story of a young detective whose career suffered a serious set-back entirely because he over-exceeded his authority. Like our friend, Sergeant Abbot, he allowed keenness to replace common sense. Make yourself comfortable and I'll begin. I heard all the facts of this tale when I was sitting on an appeal at the Crown Court. You will know that it is part of a magistrate's duty to assist a judge in hearing appeals against sentences and convictions that have been imposed by lower courts. What I am about to tell you was heard in open court so I'm not bound by the demands of confidentiality. Of course, I'll not use real names but I'll try to give you some background to the incident." I began to recount the following tale.

"Sandra was a smart young woman, about thirty years of age, a single parent, having had two children by different fathers. Both kids attended the local Church of England Infants' School. This enabled Sandra to earn a bit doing domestic cleaning and still have time to complete her own chores before school ended at a quarter to four. Life had been far from kind to her and this showed in her appearance. Although quite attractive, she had the transparent complexion and prominent cheekbones consistent with under-nourishment, an impression compounded by her lifeless hair and deep set eyes. From time to time, during the court hearing, her throaty cough revealed too close a dependence on Lady Nicotine.

Every Tuesday afternoon, having cashed her gyro cheque, she made the short trip to the centre of town to do her weekly shop at the recently opened supermarket. After snatching a quick snack, she would board the bus and look forward to two hours of browsing and perhaps even buying a few goodies for her kids.

On the afternoon in question, when she reached the top deck of the bus, anticipating a quiet smoke, she was none too pleased to discover that the only other occupant of the higher level was Jennifer, a girl with whom she was slightly acquainted. In her teenage years, Sandra had been a member of the same wild bunch as Jennifer's mum but, with the onset of parenthood, both ladies had radically adjusted their life-styles. Although the opportunity of a leisurely fag, accompanied by dreams of lavish spending, abruptly disappeared, Sandra experienced a surge of relief as she compared her own two children with the teenager now smiling eagerly at her. For the whole of her sixteen years, Jennifer had suffered massive difficulties trying to conform to the normal expectations of society. In the close-knit community of maisonettes where they lived, the older neighbours offered various opinions of, and reasons for, her disability, none of which was complimentary to either the girl or to her mother. Aware of the prejudice displayed by members of the lower classes to those even worse off than themselves, Sandra had always made an effort to be kind to Jennifer. She graciously accepted the seat, which her over-weight acquaintance had made available by shuffling her fat carcass sideways, and she offered her a cigarette.

Like Sandra, Jennifer was excited about the visit to the shops. Proudly opening her purse to reveal a cluster of coins, she boasted that it was the third time that her mum had sanctioned an unaccompanied trip. She also showed Sandra the list of four items that she had been entrusted to purchase from the very supermarket used by Sandra. What was more natural then that, after alighting at the terminus, the two females should journey together to their common destination? Sandra was maybe a little embarrassed by the incongruous appearance of her waddling companion who, to complement her unattractive figure, had a mass of unkempt hair and blotchy legs above grubby ankle socks.

At the supermarket, the teenager made a beeline for the trolleys, affording Sandra the opportunity to move off down a different aisle. Her desire to avoid spending valuable shopping time with her unpredictable acquaintance soon became a forlorn hope. After no more than fifteen precious minutes, her state of bliss was shattered by a weird howling shriek, immediately followed by the clattering of tins and the shattering of glass, then more shouting and screaming. Her curiosity overcame her natural instinct against getting involved and, leaving her partly filled trolley by the meat counter, she moved warily in the direction of the disturbance.

Rounding the end of an aisle, she came upon a veritable battle scene. The manageress and two assistants were grappling with Jennifer, primarily to prevent her from adding to the score or so of broken bottles amidst which their struggle was raging and, secondly, to arrest her pending the arrival of the police, who had been summoned by the most junior and less physically endowed member of staff. Eventually, the screaming girl was dragged up a small flight of steps to the mezzanine office overlooking the store. Sandra was still staring up at the windows of Jennifer's temporary prison when a young policewoman arrived and promptly bounded up the steps. Almost immediately, a dishevelled manageress appeared and approached Sandra.

'This crazy girl says she's with you. The officer wants you to come upstairs and calm her down.'

Sandra's response was to refuse. She knew that she had to be home by a quarter to four to be there when her children returned. Immediately, a uniformed head leaned round the threshold and sharply ordered Sandra, 'Come up here at once!' The screaming had been replaced by uncontrollable sobbing, which miraculously ceased when Jennifer saw Sandra. The policewoman explained the situation.

'This girl has stolen a large bar of chocolate, which she has consumed in the store to avoid payment. The manageress tells me that this is the third time she has done this within the past fortnight. She's taken no notice of two warnings, so that's why I've been called.'

Sandra was quick to set the position straight. 'She is not with me. I know her mum but I don't know the girl very well.' The officer's mind was made up.

'Maybe not, but look how she's settled down now that you're here.' Meanwhile, Jennifer was gripping Sandra's hand as if her life depended on it. 'I'm taking her to the station for an official caution, that's all, and I want you to assist me by accompanying us.'

'What about my kids? They'll be home before four!'

The policewoman was all reassurance. 'The desk sergeant will caution her, then, I promise, a police car will take you both home.'

With no further excuse for resistance, Sandra quickly completed her purchases and, laden with two bulging plastic bags, accompanied them to the police station. She was not a complete stranger to the establishment, having been taken there herself on two occasions in her youth for possessing cannabis. However, she had never met the desk sergeant and, when he offered her a cup of tea and politely informed her that there would be a slight delay, she took a seat in an adjacent room, glad of the chance to take the weight off her feet. As she sat there, murmuring reassurances to

Jennifer, she could not have contemplated the trauma that was about to descend upon her.

The first sign of trouble surfaced when, through the open door, she noticed Detective Constable Brian Garvey leaning across the desk sergeant's counter and ominously glancing over his shoulder at her from time to time. The two men were talking in very low tones but it was clear that there was some disagreement between them. This was confirmed when the woman police officer, whom she had assisted, joined in on the side of the sergeant. She made no effort to control the level of her voice. 'No way, Brian. She's been a big help and she's going home as soon as the girl's been cautioned.' Garvey replied in a whisper, jerking his head towards Sandra. The sergeant shrugged and the policewoman snapped out, 'I don't bloody well like it Garvey.' Calmness returned and Garvey moved away as the female officer entered the waiting room.

'Come on Jennifer, love, the sergeant wants a word with you. He won't bite. Can you bring her through, please, Sandra.' The caution was administered, care being taken to follow strictly the laid down procedures, after which the woman continued, 'That's it. Let's be off.'

The next words, spoken by D.C. Garvey, who was back on the scene, sent Sandra's heart plummeting into her boots. 'Not you, Sandra. I want a word before you go.' Sandra glanced at the desk sergeant, now conveniently engrossed in paper work. She could not hide her contempt.

'Yes, so what?'

'In there.' He pointed to the open door of an adjacent room.

'No bloody fear. Say what you've got to say out here!'

The sergeant resurfaced. 'Do as he bids, love. You can leave the door open.'

Sandra considered then, with obvious reluctance, slowly obeyed. Garvey immediately took the initiative. 'Fancy meeting you here. Being a good girl are you? Helping the Bobbies, my, my!''

'Say what you have to, Brian. I've got to get home to my kids.'

'And so you shall, my dear, as soon as you've let me have a

dekko in your purse.'

'Sod off, Garvey, I'm going.'

This was easier said than done as the burly fellow was standing between her and the doorway. He called out to his female colleague. 'Miss Jones, come in here, please.' As the embarrassed officer entered, he spoke without taking his eyes off Sandra, 'This woman is obstructing me in the course of duty. She is refusing to let me see what's in her purse.'

'For goodness sake, Sandra, let him look, then we can all go.'

'No way!'

'You see! She's obstructing a police officer. She's a druggie. I've nicked her twice!' Sandra lost her cool. 'So that's it, you creep - you think I'm handling! I only came here to help her. I want to go home to my kids.'

Ignoring her plea, Garvey lurched forward and grabbed her purse. Mayhem ensued! After a terrific struggle, he wrenched the purse from Sandra's grasp. By now, she was fighting like a tiger. Somehow, the desk sergeant, who had become involved, and the policewoman, managed to restrain her. She, for her part, was vowing to kill Garvey as the three officers lifted her on to a padded bench. Then, whilst his two colleagues held her down, the leering detective emptied the contents of her purse on to a chair, revealing nothing more sinister than a lipstick and the cash left over from her gyro.

Garvey's next order was, 'Right, let's have her boots off!' Her frantic kicking was to no avail but, again, nothing offensive was discovered. The obsessed detective had not done with her yet. His next idea was, 'You'll have to body-search her, Mabel!'

This abhorrent suggestion motivated Sandra to summon up all her remaining strength. Breaking free, she flew at Garvey and allegedly dug her teeth into his left breast. She then turned and struck Mabel a hefty blow across the face, grabbed her by the hair, and hung on until the sergeant separated them. For a time, the four of them, panting and heaving, just stared at each other. Suddenly Sandra, still grasping a fist full of hair that had recently belonged to Mabel, broke down and wept.

The sergeant took over. 'Leave her be, Brian. You, Mabel, stay with her.' Then, to the two women, 'You two, get cleaned up.'

'What about my kids, you rotten sods?'

'That's enough of that, young lady. You're going home directly. First, I'm charging you with assaulting two police officers.' "

My visitor broke his silence, "That's outrageous!"

"Maybe, but the local magistrates didn't think so. She was found guilty."

"And you sat with a judge on her appeal?"

"That's right, together with a magistrate from another court."

"I take it you granted her appeal."

"Don't jump the gun, Bobby. First of all, the judge reminded us that our task was to decide whether or not her conviction for assaulting two police officers was the correct one. In cross-examination at the appeal, Garvey failed to provide proof of the assault on him other than by his word and that of the sergeant. Mabel, the woman officer did not attend court. Apparently, she had resigned from the force soon after the incident. Garvey conceded that he had not needed to seek medical attention so there was no independent record of the bite. Neither had he arranged for the wound to be photographed and, furthermore, when it was suggested that he could open his shirt to reveal any marks which surely would still exist, he declined to do so."

"So you ruled in Sandra's favour?"

"Yes, we did. Obviously, the whole affair reflected badly on the two policemen. In the first place, they had failed to offer tangible proof of the assaults on either officer when, in Garvey's case, visual evidence of a bite could easily have been provided. Even worse, there was no dispute about the fact that Garvey had insisted on searching Sandra and her belongings, or about the improper way in which the search had been conducted. Clearly, they had allowed the young detective's keenness to prevail over their sense of propriety. Now you know why I am counselling you about the pitfalls of allowing enthusiasm to overcome good sense."

"I'll bear it in mind, Mr. Firestone...Adam. You don't mind if I call you Adam?"

CHAPTER SIX

'There is more than one way of skinning a rabbit.'

Old English proverb.

"How's the knee? The right one, wasn't it?"

"You should know. You crocked me! No, as a matter of fact, it was the left knee but it's all right now. It hasn't troubled me for years."

This pointless discussion between Peter, the vicar, and me took place in my study after school had closed one evening. The said knee belonged to me and the cause of Peter's concern harked back to a Saturday afternoon, about twenty years earlier, when we were on opposite sides in a football match, somewhere in Derbyshire. At the time, Peter was the curate of a local parish, where his active interest in youth affairs included coaching and playing for the church team.

He had moved there from his home town of Barnsley, where he had obviously developed his tackling technique by watching the local professional team, in particular a full-back called Normanton, who went by the nickname of 'Skinner', owing to the detrimental effect his close marking had on the legs of opposing wingers.

On that day, twenty years earlier, Peter and I had competed for a 'fifty-fifty' ball, which I would have been well advised to let Peter have, especially as we were leading by three goals to nil with only ten minutes to go to the final whistle. There was no question of foul play; it was just that his crunching tackle won the ball and brought a premature end to my season.

Now, here we were, two old friends, whiling away the time in innocuous conversation as we awaited the arrival of the others so that we could begin our discussion about introducing the Duke of

Edinburgh's Award scheme to Lea Grange. In order to cover the various sections of the award, I had also invited the school doctor, Jenny Keen, and my new acquaintance, Detective Constable Bobby Charlton. It was he who was responsible for our failure to start on time because although Jenny was not actually with us in my study, she was both ready and available. In fact, she was in the medical room just along the corridor, engrossed in the paper work created by the routine inspection of our second year pupils, which she had completed that day.

Jenny was a great supporter of Lea Grange, always willing to assist in all kinds of activities over and above her terms of reference. If she could spare the time to join this project, her skills, experience and connections would be invaluable. In any case, I was always pleased to welcome her into the school. Apart from her stunning good looks and attractive smile, she had a great sense of humour and she was very easy to get along with. Although small in stature and young enough to be mistaken for a student teacher, she had a quiet confidence that left no one in any doubt that she was on top of her job and certainly not to be trifled with. Furthermore, her feminine charms had a pleasing spin-off in that her visits effected a miraculous influence on the sartorial elegance of my male colleagues as well as inspiring the boys to wash behind their ears.

Nevertheless, in the past, her periodic inspections had not been entirely without their difficulties. Classes had to be rescheduled to enable youngsters to attend her clinics, although this could be accomplished fairly easily. By far the biggest problem emanated from the effect her visits had on Keith Walker, our first eleven soccer coach and self-styled Director of Football. Although well into middle age, he was still a superb performer at most games. By regular training and sensible eating he had retained the figure and mobility of a man half his age and he was well able to hold his own with the teenage boys he so successfully coached. A favourite trick was to place a separate coin on each of three cricket stumps and then to invite boys to supplement their pocket money by bowling at him. I know no instance of any boy ever penetrating his guard and collecting the cash: the outcome was a daily knockabout for Keith with an unlimited supply of leather balls for him to hammer with his trusty bat.

For Keith, each session was an ego trip. It has always saddened me that such a talented fellow's self esteem needed such regular boosting. Perhaps he was a frustrated opening batsman or perhaps he craved the fame associated with a career in professional football. Indeed, another self-glorification ruse was to imply that he was a personal friend of the manager of Chelsea Football Club. To support this claim, every Monday morning, he treated his colleagues to a detailed report of Chelsea's match of the previous Saturday. This was supposedly based on an alleged telephone discussion with his manager friend who, having reported the game in detail, would seek Keith's advice on the composition of the team and on tactics for the next match. It is remarkable that not a single one of us who, like Keith, also had access to the soccer bulletins in the Sunday newspapers, ever said, 'Pull the other leg, Keith.'

Sadly, he did not confine his romanticising to tales of civilian life, frequently treating his colleagues to unbelievable accounts of his exploits whilst serving in the Royal Air Force during World War Two. The word 'unbelievable' is deliberately chosen because, owing to the flatness of his feet or some other incongruous ailment, Keith never entered the armed forces. The nearest he came to combat was as a station officer in the auxiliary fire service in Cheltenham.

This did not deter him from recounting how, as a squadron-leader, he frequently turned the tables on the Luftwaffe, not only by shooting down their planes but how, by using the tips of his Spitfire's wings, he redirected Hitler's dreaded flying bombs, turning them round to fly back and blow up their own launching sites.

There was one story, which did amuse me and, I suppose, was just about within the bounds of possibility. However, not having served in the forces, Keith must have heard it from a third party or, more likely, made it up.

It concerned a young corporal who worked as a pay-accounts clerk on a large airfield in eastern England. Fond of wine and women (song was not mentioned), he was always in debt by the time payday dawned, that is, until he devised a 'fool-proof' scheme! Quite brazenly, he 'created' a small section of eight men who were supposedly 'based' at a small satellite station in the heart of rural Lincolnshire. He drew up the obligatory register of their number, rank and name, worked out the fortnightly remuneration due to each individual and, every two weeks, personally withdrew the total amount of cash he needed to pay them. It was his responsibility to take the money by motorcycle to the section of airmen that his devious mind had invented.

He successfully operated the scheme for the last eighteen months of his service career. It was only when he threw a lavish demobilisation party for himself, to which he invited all the top brass from his squadron, that tongues began to wag and suspicions were aroused. The inevitable investigation caused immense embarrassment for his immediate superior, the Accounts Officer, and it resulted in a five-year sentence for the ingenious, if misguided, young corporal.

Clearly, talented as he was, the fact that Keith Walker felt compelled to weave such incredible yarns indicated that he was chronically insecure. That was why the doctor's visits undermined his pretence of importance. On assuming the illustrious title of Director of Football, he had established an efficient coaching and treatment set-up over which he reigned. In reality, it was a facade, a vehicle of self-aggrandisement for its founder. Nevertheless, I was grateful to Keith for the benefits enjoyed by innumerable boys.

One may wonder, then, how the visits of the delightful doctor could have had such a devastating effect on an eminent person like Keith. In fact, they had done so in two ways.

The greatest difficulty emanated from Keith's use of the medical room as his base. Over the years, he had accumulated all kinds of equipment and preparations relating to the treatment of sports injuries, not the least of which was a massive heat lamp. This gem was in almost constant use, administering to the pulled muscles and strained limbs of our intrepid football and lacrosse players. Then there were the bottles, in particular the one containing liniment, which emitted such a powerful and pungent smell that a blind man could have found his way to the medical room from a radius of fifty yards.

When the doctor visited, all these trappings had to be relocated in the much smaller library storeroom, which was the other niche that Keith had somehow acquired. It goes without saying that Bill Brown, the school keeper, had the formidable task of ridding the medical room of the telltale odours. Of course, the relative positions of Keith and the doctor in the hierarchy were apparent to all. There was no contest, nor should there have been, but somehow our hero was always visibly upset when he had to release the medical room so that it could be used in accordance with its proper designation.

Not surprisingly, the charming doctor had not needed ultra-sensitive antennae to recognise the problem. She was extremely kind and understanding about it. In the confines of my study, she and I would have a chuckle about Keith's fragile ego but in public she was magnificent in the way she handled the situation. She always took the trouble to ask him how 'his' teams were faring and if she could be of any help in cases of injury to key players. To some extent, this exacerbated the problem in that it indicated that he, normally a big noise, was in second place to a slip of a girl, so the pleasures that my colleagues and I derived from the doctor's visitations were always tinged with apprehension as to how Keith Walker would react. In the past, I had never been able to look forward unreservedly to welcoming Florence Nightingale's successor into Lea Grange. Thankfully, the problem had been solved almost at a stroke during a medical inspection several months earlier.

On that auspicious day the doctor and her assistant drove into the parking space that was always reserved for their vehicle. They were immediately greeted by a multitude of small boys, all eager to open doors and to serve as porters for the two popular ladies.

Once relieved of their cases and after the usual pleasantries came the enquiry, "How's Keith? Is he still with you?" I nodded as she went on, "Don't look so worried, Adam. I think I shall be able to win him over this time!" She did not elaborate and I did not press her.

All became clear on the last lunchtime of her visit. I came upon the two of them, busily engaged in animated conversation as they shared the midday meal.

"Please join us, Adam. Keith and I were just tying up one or two loose ends. The inspections will be finished by the end of the afternoon, so you'll be rid of me for a while, at least." Whilst I was pondering what the 'one or two loose ends' could be, she explained the miracle she had performed.

Apparently, her thirteen-year-old son, Francis, had been called into the County junior soccer squad. Naturally, both she and his father were overjoyed but they were realistic enough to realise that, although he was endowed with natural ball-playing skills, he was a novice with regard to positional play. This had not been a problem when he had played in his school team, where he was the star. However, his father was afraid that this weakness would be a severe handicap to him at a higher level. Thus the expert assistance of Keith had been respectfully solicited and he had readily agreed to teach Francis the rudiments of tactics.

"Oh, and by the way, who's been making Keith move his tackle out of the medical room every time I visit?" Keith shuffled awkwardly and his cheeks flushed. After an embarrassed pause, he plucked up courage to explain,

"Yes, Headmaster, Jenny says she's quite happy for me to continue the lunch-time sessions when she's with us. Oh, and she's had a look at young Thompson's ankle and she's ruled him out of Saturday's semi-final."

I remember thinking, "Jenny and Keith now, is it? You artful little minx. I only hope he doesn't try to sign you on as Chelsea's club doctor!" More to the point, as Peter and I waited for Bobby Charlton, I just hoped that I could secure my three friends' support for our latest project.

Eventually, the detective arrived, full of apologies. Ironically, the cause of his lateness was educational in that he had been directed to deal with an unwelcome intruder at Greenfield School:

an assault by an angry parent on a member of the staff.

"You can tell me about it later," I suggested. "We must not keep the doctor and the vicar waiting any longer."

I quickly outlined the aims and workings of the award scheme before explaining how I considered each one of them could contribute. Whilst we at school could be fully responsible for the Physical Recreation section, their help with the Service and Skills sections would be invaluable. In addition, Bobby's knowledge of outdoor pursuits would be very useful when it came to organising the expedition.

Although I was not entirely surprised when all three displayed enthusiasm equal to mine, I was nevertheless both delighted and relieved. I undertook to make the necessary arrangements and to contact them when we were ready to begin. I had been involved with the Scheme since its inception in 1956 and I had learned through experience that careful planning was essential. There was a great deal of work ahead of us before we would be presenting candidates for the Gold Award at Buckingham Palace!

I was determined to get the project off to a good start and to avoid such mishaps as had befallen us at the inner-city school, where I had served as Deputy-Headmaster, several years earlier. I had introduced the Award Scheme there but only for the boys. My insensitivity deserved the understandable response from Dorothy, the music mistress, who firmly declared that whatever boys could do; their sisters could do just as well, or even better!

There was no logical reason for me to disagree with this noble sentiment. Indeed, I was delighted when she went further by offering to organise the training of the girls. Unfortunately, I could not begin to imagine what we were letting ourselves in for. The whole affair requires a chapter to itself!

CHAPTER SEVEN

'Anything you can do, I can do better,
I can do anything better than you.
No you can't!
Yes I can, yes I can, yes I can!'

Irving Berlin.

When Dorothy issued her challenge that girls were equally as capable as boys were to undertake the rigours of the Duke of Edinburgh's Award, I was in full agreement with her. Furthermore, when she volunteered to take responsibility for their training, I was delighted, yet, even then, I did have certain misgivings with regard to her all-round suitability. I could not fault her commitment: it was her tendency to over-indulge her classes that worried me. A well-built spinster, she often bemoaned the fact that, "The men don't appreciate my ample charms!"

Every morning, she would arrive at school on her motorbike, clad in trench coat and helmet, invariably cheered through the gates by her approving pupils. At weekends, she exchanged this 'uniform' for that of the St. John's Ambulance Brigade. It was a unique experience to hear her strident rendering of 'Cherry Ripe' or to join her in song, vigorously asking, 'What shall we do with a drunken sailor early in the morning?' Yes, the kids loved their music periods but I'm not sure it was for the right reasons.

My concern was that she was not sufficiently aloof to be able to control a group of high-spirited youngsters away from the secure umbrella of the school and, therefore, I was greatly relieved to learn that Mary, a young teacher keen on geography, had offered to assist Dorothy with the Expedition. The offer was subject to a single condition: that the two naughtiest girls in the school, Elaine Palmer and Brenda Jones, definitely would not be going. This assurance given, the small party of bona-fide girls was advised about suitable footwear, clothing, and provisions for the self-catering weekend. At break time on the Friday afternoon, Dorothy dropped her bombshell: Brenda and Elaine had solemnly promised to be good if she would let them go along and she had been persuaded.

"But they don't even want to do the Duke of Edinburgh's Award. They only want to go to lark about!" exploded Mary. "If it wasn't so far advanced, I'd pull out."

"I'm sorry but they've already told their parents. I'm sure they won't be any trouble," was the lame response. It was with an air of foreboding that the angry Mary left school that night. True, no longer was either of the two on probation as were several of their classmates. However, no reassurance could be drawn from this considering that, respectively, they had only just completed periods of six months and one year for shoplifting and for making hoax calls to the fire brigade.

Brenda was the light-fingered one - extremely skilled in obtaining goods without payment. Her two favoured stores were Woolworth's and C. & A., the first to obtain a regular supply of sundries and the second to equip herself and trusted 'customers' with clothes for going out. Until the uncooperative behaviour of the toddler from next door brought about her downfall, she had built up quite a lucrative little business, supplying selected items to order at knock-down prices. Oh yes, her 'customers' would pay a visit to the store to check over the items on offer, then they would supply Brenda with details such as size and colour, leaving the rest to her.

Smaller than average for her age, our anti-heroine, modestly dressed in neatly buttoned coat with Peter Pan collar, her eager, wide-eyed face devoid of any traces of make-up, would use a variety of techniques to ply her illegal trade. Her most favoured method was to offer to take the little boy from next door for a walk in his pushchair, a request invariably granted by his overwrought mother.

Having used this ploy with resounding success on numerous occasions, Brenda was both unprepared and shocked when, as they passed through the swing doors on their way out of the store, little Johnny plucked a brand new cardigan from beneath the apron of his pushchair and flung it on to the ground. Unfortunately, a sales assistant witnessed the incident and, when several other items were discovered hidden under the apron, Brenda was well and truly caught.

Sadly, rather than showing remorse, she cursed herself for allowing greed to lead her into carelessness. The fact of the matter was that when she had conceived the idea of using the toddler and his pushchair, she had had a dual purpose in mind: a kind of insurance policy. Obviously, the chair with an apron was a good place to secrete the stolen articles but, of even greater importance, if she were stopped and searched, she could deny all knowledge of any theft by suggesting that little Johnny must have picked up the item when her attention was otherwise engaged.

This explanation might have worked on her earlier forays, when she had confined her shoplifting to a single item, but success had fostered avarice and increased her boldness. Thus, on the day she was apprehended, there were no fewer than six articles of clothing tucked around the toddler's knees. The local constabulary were grateful when she agreed to up-grade their detection rate by opting to have fourteen previous offences of stealing taken into consideration and, in view of this 'frank and truthful' admission, they did not press her when she was unable to recall where and how she had disposed of the proceeds of her earlier thefts. There was no opposition to a six-month probation order.

In contrast to Brenda, Elaine never dressed down or went out without make-up. She was always on the lookout for 'fellas'. Tall and well built with well-groomed auburn hair, of above-average intelligence, it could be said that she had everything going for her. She appeared to have a cold, arrogant disposition and generally did not seek the friendship of girls. Her only companion was Brenda, although she had had several boyfriends in the school before she took to associating with older men.

In fact, it was this change in her taste towards males that brought about the discovery that she was the perpetrator of the nuisance calls, which brought a regular stream of bell-ringing fire engines to the neighbourhood. The calls were made from a variety of telephone kiosks at intervals of ten days or so. After five or six hoax calls had been answered, a member of the fire-brigade called in at the school, informing us that the calls were being made by a female with a 'young sounding' voice and requesting our assistance in identifying the culprit.

Our Headmaster appealed for information at assembly on the following day without response. It was 'Falstaff', our rotund Head of English, who made the breakthrough. A few days after the unsuccessful assembly appeal, he had used 'Disasters' as the theme for a series of lessons involving poetry, prose, debate, and creative writing. Apparently, one of the discussions had developed along rather gruesome lines and the disastrous results of hoax calls to emergency services that have occurred in real life were examined with no punches pulled.

After he had dismissed the class, Falstaff became aware of a gangling youth lingering at the back of the room, seemingly waiting until the coast was clear. When he was satisfied that he was alone with the teacher, the lad admitted that he knew who was making the calls. He supplied enough evidence to convict Elaine, who was given a severe dressing down by the magistrates together with a twelve-month probation order. Later, Falstaff discovered that his informant was a spurned ex-boyfriend who had been devastated when Elaine had developed a preference for the more mature males of the species.

Returning to the account of the expedition, Saturday dawned bright and sunny, and a motley crew in ill-assorted gear assembled early at the bus station. Miraculously, no one was late. The two renegades were trying to keep a low profile, partly because they were carrying a large portable radio. It had not occurred to Mary that anyone would be stupid enough to bring such an item. Once the two were on the upper deck of the bus, the windows were immediately opened, scarves hung out and the radio switched on. Mary had to move into top gear to control the unruly mob and prevent the other passengers from complaining.

After enduring several miles of unease, the two teachers were relieved to alight with their charges on to the open moors, where the hike began. Although they had been issued with maps, the girls were to be walking within sight of the road, as this was their first experience of rambling. It was then that Mary noticed the footwear of the terrible pair: stiletto heels below tight skirts.

"How on earth can you possibly hike in those?" she wailed. "You'd better walk at the edge of the road, where it's flat." At least, they couldn't get lost! Dorothy and Mary set off in silence, endeavouring to keep an eye on both sets of girls.

Within fifteen minutes, the two bringing up the rear of the main party, Ruth and Sandra, were uttering cries of, "Can we have a rest?" and, "This bag's too heavy." When the teachers caught up with them, they were seated on large rocks, their bags dumped on the nearby heath.

"Come on, we've a long way to go," said Mary, yanking up one of the bags. "Good heavens, what on earth is in here?" she demanded, dropping it just as quickly. Peering into it, she saw that it contained no less than six large bottles of lemonade. "I just do not believe this!" she exclaimed.

"Well, you said to decide what we were going to eat and drink and share it out amongst ourselves. I bagged bringing the drink," was Ruth's sulky response.

"I also told you to bring meals that would be light to carry," replied Mary wearily. "And what have you got in your bag, Sandra?"

Sandra fixed her eyes stubbornly on the distant horizon and so, in desperation, Dorothy lifted the top flap of the haversack. She burst out laughing.

"A five pound bag of potatoes!"

"So...I was going to make chips and I needed enough spuds for everybody," shouted Sandra, defensively. From the dark patch spreading at the bottom of the bag, there was no need to enquire from where she was getting the fat.

As the rest of the group were too far forward to call back and the terrible twins, who had disregarded the instruction to walk facing the on-coming traffic, were dawdling behind, Mary and Dorothy off-loaded some potatoes and a couple of bottles into their own bags and the foursome trudged on. The lightening of the loads lifted Ruth and Sandra's spirits considerably and their lively chatter and jibes helped to pass the time. Mary began to feel more relaxed, as she looked forward to the picnic she and Dorothy would share round about midday.

The fact that so little traffic had passed along the distant road all morning made the sudden blare of a musical motor horn all the more startling. Jerked out of their private thoughts, the teachers turned in unison to behold an open tourer speeding along with their two problem pupils waving enthusiastically from the comfort of the rear seat. Hopes that they would be kidnapped and sold as white slaves were quickly replaced by fears that they might be. Heavens, what if they were never seen again? There was only one thing to do. They must hurry on to the appointed meeting place and, if the two did not show up, ring the youth hostel and then the police.

The anxious pair set off, soon leaving behind their erstwhile hiking companions. Rapidly overtaking the advanced group, potatoes and bottles notwithstanding, they covered the ground at a good army route-marching pace. At long last, Hathersage came into view and Mary could not believe how pleased she was to come upon Brenda and Elaine sitting on a bench in the centre of the village, licking ice-cream cornets. Relief was quickly replaced by anger as, barely able to keep her hands off them, she ordered them to go immediately up the long road to the Hostel.

What should have been a relatively pleasant couple of days amid the beautiful Derbyshire countryside, breathing the fresh air and cementing friendships with their enthusiastic charges, was rapidly deteriorating into a nightmare. Mary could not help cursing herself for being foolish enough to be duped by Dorothy. The fact that her assistance had been obtained under false pretences was irrelevant. If they were to emerge relatively unscathed by the events of the next twenty-four hours, she would have to assume the control that her colleague had never enjoyed.

Once they were in the confines of the hostel, close supervision was the order of the day. It was fortunate that Mary gave her full attention to the chip pan because the two appointed cooks were oblivious to the dangers of hot fat. Eventually, after Mary had had a quiet nervous breakdown, a passable meal was produced and eagerly devoured. Coercion became the byword to make sure the kitchen was cleared and Dorothy hovered by the door to ensure that nobody 'skived off' without doing their share. Mary was equally determined that no one would get the chance of disappearing to join the Saturday night revels at the local pubs by insisting that all eight girls remained in the common room, making do for entertainment with various games and an ancient record player.

It was not the kind of evening that Brenda and Elaine were used to but they were well and truly trapped. Dinner completed, they escaped into the toilets, and after an interminable fifteen minutes Mary decided to investigate. Guided by the twin columns of smoke rising from the end cubicle, it was not difficult to ascertain the location of the pair. They were unceremoniously yanked out and stood blinking, clown-like in their green sparkle eyeshadow and garish lipstick. They must have been very disappointed that their cosmetic efforts were to be wasted, the only males on the premises being a disapproving warden and a party of twelve-year-old boy scouts, who were intimidated rather than attracted by the stiletto-heeled vamps.

Bedtime and lights-out could not come too soon for the two 'leaders', who had been allocated a small room adjacent to the girls' dormitory. At least any misbehaviour could be contained without other hostellers being disturbed. Exhaustion took over and both Dorothy and Mary were soon asleep...but not for long! Just before midnight, the warden's banging on the girls' door and calling for quiet awakened them. Incensed and still half-asleep, Mary leapt off her top bunk oblivious to the semi-transparency of her short nightie and charged into the next room. She was drowned by a clamour of noise as the six committed hikers screamed at the two renegades to stop fooling around and get into bed. At Mary's abrupt appearance, Brenda moved like lightning towards her bed but the less-speedy Elaine was treated to a spanking as she scampered hither and thither, eventually reaching the sanctuary of the top bunk. All frivolity and giggles were suppressed as Mary threatened to come down like a ton of bricks on anyone foolish enough to transgress further.

"Thanks Mary, sleep tight," were the last words Dorothy uttered before her regular breathing signified the onset of deep sleep, no doubt the result of the unaccustomed exertion of the day. Meanwhile, back on the top bunk, her exasperated colleague fumed restlessly.

A loud knock on their door accompanied by a cheerful, "Good morning, Misses," heralded the start of another potentially disastrous day. Breaking her personal speed record for washing and dressing, Mary was soon in the kitchen, determined that the breakfast preparations would not end in mayhem. She was conscious that only her timely intervention the previous evening had prevented a fire during the cooking of the infamous chips.

During the meal, during which a noisy debate ensued on who was the most to blame for the previous night's escapades, the warden arrived to allocate their chores. Beds had to be made up, rooms and corridors swept and breakfast pots washed. Predictably, the group's departure was delayed because the two nuisances had to repeat their tasks, the first efforts having failed to satisfy the warden.

Eventually, they all assembled in the yard at the front of the hostel clutching much lighter burdens, the original contents having been devoured ravenously, and they embarked upon the supervised trek that would take them through Bamford and Castleton to the Winnats Pass. Once there, their assignment was to look for a suitable campsite for when they undertook the expedition in earnest. Next time it would be under canvas.

The six relatively reliable girls were dispatched at intervals in pairs but Brenda and Elaine were made to walk with the adults. It was obvious that their unsuitable footwear was playing havoc with their poor feet and, given half a chance, they would have begged another lift. Mary, who kept the two within her reach at all times, forestalled any such move.

The hike was not the pleasant stroll that it should have been but, after three miserable hours, they attained their objective without mishap. It was probably the absence of any problem since they had left the hostel that encouraged Dorothy to adopt a bold and assertive stance. "Right girls, take thirty minutes. Have your picnic, then we'll find a campsite. Carry on."

Whilst Mary was wondering why Dorothy could not always be so positive, they were interrupted with; "Please Miss, Elaine and Brenda have gone into a cave with some big lads."

"A cave? Lads? There's nobody about except us," observed Dorothy with more hope than conviction.

"Where are they?" demanded Mary.

"Up there, Miss. Are you going in after them?"

Ignoring the question, Mary picked her way up over the stony ground towards the cave entrance and announced to all inside, "I am now going to the bus stop. I've got all the money. Anybody who does not get on the bus with me will have to walk home." Her voice echoed in the pitch darkness but there was no reply, no sign of life within.

Undaunted, she marched purposefully down the pathway followed by the rest of the girls with Dorothy bringing up the rear.

"We can't leave them, Mary."

"Be quiet and keep walking. Don't look round."

After a few hundred yards, Mary stooped to tie her shoelace. A quick glance told her what she had hoped for. Brenda and Elaine were slowly emerging from the mouth of the cave and were being helped over the rough ground by three older youths. Mary strode out intending to make for the nearest bus stop from which to end this hopeless exercise. The rest of the dejected party trailed behind over a distance of a quarter of a mile, eventually catching up with Mary at Bamford. As there were few buses on Sundays, she had kept them walking until the time that one was due.

The return journey was completed in a more subdued atmosphere as our two anti-heroines had got the message that 'Miss' had reached the end of her tether and they dare not risk being put off the bus unceremoniously. Mary was disappointed that the weekend had not been a success and she felt sorry for the six girls whose adventure she had unilaterally curtailed. What was more, she had wasted her own weekend, which could have been used to store up energy to face the impending rigours of a new week. The last straw came on the Monday morning when the incorrigible pair bounced up to Mary, exclaiming, "It were great, Miss, when can we go again?"

For the record, five of the six serious contenders persevered and, by eventually obtaining the Bronze Award, proved Dorothy's claim that girls could match their brothers in adventurous activities. As for Mary, she never again volunteered her own free time to out of school trips without first agreeing on the participants.

POST SCRIPT TO CHAPTER SEVEN

'All's well that ends well.'

Corroboration for Dorothy's bold assertion with regard to the relative merits of girls vis-à-vis boys emerged in a somewhat negative fashion. One Friday evening, about a month after the infamous weekend, six eager boys and their equipment piled into the school minibus for the trip to Edale in the Peak District. Having completed the other sections of the Bronze Award, they were about to undertake the final test: the Expedition.

The arrangement was for them to camp as a group on the first night then, divided into three couples, follow different trails for seven or eight miles, camp overnight on the Saturday and report back to base at Edale by three o'clock the following day. The three separate routes had been chosen by Harry, our Games master who, as an assistant Scoutmaster, was a regular visitor to the Derbyshire countryside. Sketch maps had been prepared and the boys were required to answer questions about certain landmarks they would encounter on their prescribed route. In all three cases, a suitable place for the overnight camp was clearly marked.

This latter stipulation was to serve two purposes. In the first place, it would test whether or not the boys were capable of following a simple map but, of greater importance, it would enable Harry and me to check that they were progressing safely on their respective journeys. In the case of one couple, it proved to be a wise precaution.

The two lads concerned were an interesting pair in that their friendship had developed comparatively recently, to the great benefit of the younger one, a freckle-faced red-haired boy who, not surprisingly, suffered the nickname 'Carrots'. He had joined our school two years earlier at the age of thirteen, accompanied by the thickest portfolio on a youngster that I have ever been obliged to read. It comprised a mixture of reports and medical opinions based on the results of numerous psychological tests, all transmitting the same message: Carrots was a disturbed individual and, so far, nobody he had encountered in his young life had been able to do anything about it. His unacceptable behaviour had been apparent from the day he commenced his formal education in the local infants' school and, when it was clear that his bad behaviour defied normal control, he was bundled off to a special centre for individual assessment and treatment, again without any tangible success.

Residential care followed and, by the time he was admitted into our school, he had spent a total of eight years in no fewer than three boarding establishments. Eventually, when it was apparent that some of the most skilled practitioners in the land were making no progress with him, his parents withdrew him from his most recent placement in North Yorkshire and presented him at the door of his nearest comprehensive school, which happened to be ours!

On his first morning, before we had had the opportunity to unseal his file, let alone read it, he was placed in the tutor group of Janet, a quietly spoken lady who had already survived ten or eleven years in our challenging place of work. She had been there long enough to know the elder brothers and sisters of her present group, most of whom regarded her as a mother figure. She loved them, rogues and all. She was proud of them, she provided them with a happy and secure learning environment, and they repaid her with respect and, generally, good behaviour.

Thus, she was astounded when, at morning break, Carrots, who had been in her charge for less than two hours, cruelly disturbed the civilised orderly atmosphere of her form room. He did so by hitting the girl seated in front of him over the head with the bottle from which he had just consumed his mid-morning milk. The piercing scream of the injured party had the effect on her classmates similar to that of a fox that has broken into a coop full of hens.

Janet's astonishment was quickly replaced by genuine anger as she comprehended the seriousness of the situation. Faced with the choice of comforting the little girl or dealing with Carrots, she opted for the latter. Leaping from her seat, she grabbed him by the scruff of the neck and jerked him to the front of the class, where she administered three resounding thwacks on his buttocks with her hitherto unused cane.

Such a sanction is no longer available to the teaching profession; some think it should be, others disagree. All I know is that, where seven or eight years of psychological treatment had seemingly had no effect on Carrots, the mental and physical impact of Janet's summary justice worked wonders. From that day henceforth, he settled down and never put a foot wrong during his remaining time at the school.

The fact that Stewart, one of our most promising lads, formed a close friendship with Carrots was testimony to the latter's positive development. This is how they came to be partners on their Duke of Edinburgh expedition that particular weekend and how they subscribed to Dorothy's assertion that anything boys can do girls can do just as well. On this occasion, they did so in a sort of reverse way by proving that boys can mess up a situation equally as well as their sisters.

The first sign of trouble surfaced when they failed to turn up at the designated camping place on the Saturday evening, even though the site had been clearly indicated on their map. Harry had carefully planned each of the three expeditions so that the overnight camps were within a four-mile radius of the main road. This would enable him to check that the lads were safe and allow him to assess how each couple was coping. Young and fit, it was a pleasant and varied way for him to do his daily 'work-out'.

Thus, my Saturday evening was ruined when he telephoned to report his anxieties. "I've run a million miles, combed the area with a fine tooth comb! There's absolutely no sign of them."

"What about the other two couples?"

"They were both fine...spot on with their map-reading and well into cooking their meals. I can't understand what has happened to the other two silly beggars."

"Well, it's dark now. We can do nothing more until morning."

"It's just that it is very easy to get lost in the Peak District. A bomber crashed somewhere there in the Second World War and it was not discovered until years later."

"Don't be a Job's comforter, Harry. Look, you have done all you can. I'll drive over to Edale at first light and make another search." Harry insisted on coming with me and the two of us were on the moors at the crack of dawn. We followed their specified route with meticulous care but, when we reached the allotted campsite without finding any evidence of them, our worst fears began to increase. There was not even a sweet wrapper; they had vanished without trace!

My companion was thinking aloud, no doubt to reassure both of us. "Stew is a sensible lad. He'll know what to do, even if one of them is lying injured."

I kept my thoughts to myself. "Thank you, Harry, for being so bloody cheerful but I had not even considered such a grotesque eventuality!"

We completed our journey to Edale by following separate paths in order to cover as much of the area as possible but we arrived at our meeting place no wiser than when we had set out.

"If they don't appear by two o'clock, I shall report them missing at the Peak Warden's office."

"Don't worry, I'm sure they will be all right," replied my fellow-sufferer.

And they were!

"Where the heck have you two been?" yelled Harry, as the shame-faced pair came into view across a neighbouring field, well before the arranged time.

"We must have got lost, Sir. I think we chose the wrong path early on," explained Stewart.

Harry was not impressed. "That, my lad, would be obvious to an imbecile!" was his sarcastic retort. Personally, I was too relieved to be annoyed.

I almost laughed when Carrots asked, with the innocence of a babe, "Have we passed, Sir? We made camp like you taught us and we cooked a lovely dinner."

"Passed? Passed?" screeched Harry, screwing up his face in pain. "I'll give you passed! I've spent my weekend looking for you two idiots. Of course you haven't passed, you stupid boy! A couple of ten-year-old lasses could do better than you two!"

Yes, Dorothy, your point is conceded. Anything we can do, you can do better!

CHAPTER EIGHT

'Why beholdest thou the mote that is in thy brother's eye, but considerest not the beam that is in thine own eye?'

St. Matthew 7 iii.

"I don't care whether you are in Beckbridge, Manchester or Majorca; if you misbehave and let us all down at Lea Grange, then you will have me to answer to."

Standing in my elevated position on the stage of the assembly hall, resplendent in academic gown, I would tuck my thumbs under the shoulder straps and allow a dramatic pause for the message to be thoroughly digested by my captive audience.

"Lea Grange is one of the finest schools in Great Britain and you are all very lucky to be able to study here." Another pause, "But, girls and boys, privilege demands responsibility: wherever in the world you are, your conduct must be above reproach. Any bad behaviour will bring discredit upon our school. Never forget that."

Was I deluding myself? Did I detect smiles of pride on the eager, shining faces of my assembled pupils? Was it my imagination or did their collective chins project a little, albeit almost imperceptibly? Did their chests expand as I lavished praise upon the wonderful school that they were all fortunate enough to attend? Was I deceiving myself? I think not. Certainly not, according to the regular feedback that I received from a variety of sources.

Over many years, innumerable parents have expressed their satisfaction at the attitude their sons and daughters have exhibited towards Lea Grange: a mixture of loyalty, camaraderie, and trust. Scores of ex-students, many well into adulthood, assure me how proud they were to wear the school uniform.

I have long believed that a school is as good as its reputation, as good as it is perceived by its members and by the wider community. I have always believed, also, that the most direct route to establishing a good reputation for a school is through its pupils and their parents. The strategy is not complicated: encourage the development of pride in the institution; value the opportunities on offer; foster respect through good behaviour; and, finally, come down heavily on those who transgress.

Of course, my philosophy was well known to pupils and their parents and, indeed to many in the Beckbridge public. I even indoctrinated my fellow Rotarians so that I was invariably introduced to visitors as the "Headmaster of one of the best schools in the North-West". This was particularly advantageous if I happened to be talking to industrialists and other potential employers of my pupils.

Thus, in view of my efforts to develop good public relations, it came as quite a shock to me when, during a parents' consultation evening, a lively young mother announced, "You seemed to be enjoying yourself on the Costa with your drunken friend, last Easter, Mr. Firestone!"

I recognised the proprietor of the local tobacconist shop, which doubled as a sub-post office: a formidable lady who was known to all and sundry as 'The eyes and ears of the world'.

"I'm sorry, I don't know what you mean, Mrs. Parker? Why don't you come into my study and have a seat? You must tell me more." I confess that my prime object was to remove this purveyor of information away from the earshot of other parents. I was less concerned about her personal comfort. After all, if my students were expected to behave themselves in Majorca, I must do likewise on the Spanish Mainland. I certainly could not allow anyone to suggest that the standard of my own conduct had ever fallen below that which I demanded of my pupils.

Once we were seated at my coffee table, a tactic I employed to put visitors at ease, I smiled an invitation for Mrs. Parker to do her worst. She certainly tried!

"It was when Mr. Parker and I were on holiday in Spain last

Easter. We called in at the Belvedere for a nightcap. It was quite a sight to see the three of you staggering up the stairs to bed."

Although several months had elapsed, my heart missed a few beats when I recalled the incident to which she was referring. I did not doubt that an embellished version had already been relayed on numerous occasions to anyone in need of postage stamps, pensions, or cigarettes. Almost all of her customers would have heard the saga of Mr. and Mrs. Firestone and their drunken friend living it up on the Costa Blanca.

My visitor was correct in her supposition that I had enjoyed my holiday but the rest of her impression was completely inaccurate. The episode that she had witnessed was nothing more than an unwelcome diversion, but I knew that I would have an uphill task trying to convince her of this.

To begin with, Martin was neither my friend nor was he a typical drunk. Indeed, although I had only made his acquaintance two days earlier, when he and his wife had joined us for an aperitif in the hotel bar, I would wager that he had never been drunk before that infamous occasion, nor will he ever allow himself to succumb again.

It was the fact that he had been brought up in the Beckbridge Valley that drew us together. "Would you believe it? What a small world!" we all exclaimed.

His family owned a paper mill near Preston and so, after public school, he had moved from the Valley to live nearer to the business in order to take over from his father as managing director. He travelled widely for the firm; I recall him relating a spooky tale about his room at the Plaza Hotel, New York, being broken into and robbed whilst he and his wife slept. Their present visit to the Belvedere Hotel had been to enable them to inspect work that was being carried out to the plumbing of their holiday home, a few miles along the coast. Apparently, it had been much cheaper to arrange an all-in package to a hotel than to pay for a scheduled flight.

Martin and Marion were a very respectable, well-connected couple and extremely interesting conversationalists. The incident witnessed by the Parkers was completely out of character. Nevertheless, I could well understand how they had formed their wrong impression.

On the morning of the day that progressed into such an embarrassing evening for me, my newly found friends had hired a car to visit their property. This task completed, and satisfied that the progress on the plumbing was acceptable, they had decided to call in at a local bar to surprise the proprietor and the regular clientele, among whom they could count many friends made during their regular visits to the area. That day, everyone in the village seemed to be present and most insisted on toasting the unexpected arrival of their English amigos. One drink had led to many more, the company was agreeable, they laughed a lot, discrimination weakened and, uncontrollably, their state progressed from happiness to drunkenness.

Martin could not recall the journey back to the hotel. I deliberately avoid describing it as 'the drive back' because the final part of it was on foot. At some stage, even in his confused state of mind, he must have realised that, for the safety of all around as well as for his own sake, he would have to abandon the vehicle. If that was good news, the bad news was that, on the following morning, he had no recollection of where he and his wife had baled out. Consequently, instead of being able to sleep off his hangover, he had to tramp around the neighbourhood until, after three hours or more of torture, he came across it, clumsily parked, unlocked but, mercifully, undamaged.

My wife, Jane, and I were drawn into the problem from the moment that Martin appeared at the lounge door in what can only be described as a thoroughly dishevelled state. Barely able to remain upright without the aid of the doorpost, rocking gently to and fro, he raised his hand as if to shield his eyes, sailor-like, and deliberately scanned the large room. From time to time, he shuffled sideways to allow people to pass, bowing in mock reverence to the ladies, before resuming his visual exploration of the social gathering. Clearly, he was searching for someone, most likely his wife, I remember hoping.

We were seated at a table in the furthest corner from the door. There was a good chance that he would not see us, or so we hoped. No such luck! The gradual appearance of a silly grin on his befuddled countenance indicated that he had recognised somebody. The hand that he was using to shield his eyes began waving wildly and, when the other occupants of the lounge all turned to look in our direction, we feared the worst. I hesitate to say that he had focused on us; many hours would pass before he would be capable of focusing on anything.

Through bleary eyes, he measured the distance between his position in the doorway and our table, taking note of any obstacles that lay in between. Then, he lurched forward into the room, half weaving, half staggering, narrowly avoiding tables covered with bottles and glasses, almost falling, then stumping to a halt to regain his balance, occasionally raising an imaginary hat to the occupants of adjacent tables. He somehow completed his journey across the floor and toppled into the soft cushions of a settee opposite us.

I suppose that if the Parkers had entered the lounge after Martin had joined us, they could not help drawing the wrong conclusions. He certainly was a mess with unkempt hair, unbuttoned shirt, slackened tie, and with blood dripping from his left sleeve. Almost collapsing on to the coffee table as he leaned forward, he announced, "You won't believe it. I've fallen through the window!" Then, dabbing his wrist with the handkerchief I had offered him, he hailed a passing waiter with, "Three brandies my man."

I immediately amended the order to three coffees, one without milk, completely ignoring Martin's loud protests. Thankfully, the waiter followed my instructions rather than my friend's.

"Now Martin, tell us what you've been up to."

"I said you wouldn't believe it. I've fallen through the bloody window!"

"Martin, listen. Where's Marion?"

"Marion's my wife. I love her."

"Yes, we know. But where is she?"

He placed his forefinger over his pursed lips and, assuming a conspiratorial air, he whispered, "She's in bed. Shhh!" Then, more in shock than hilarity, he giggled, "You won't believe it. I've fallen through the window." The coffee arrived and the three of us studiously concentrated our attention on it. My mind was working overtime. I allowed Martin to stir in two lumps of sugar, then I enquired, "Which window?"

"The door leading on to the balcony. There's glass all over the place." He chuckled, "Marion doesn't know, she's asleep in bed."

A furtive glance round the room reassured me that our fellow guests had resumed their social activities centred on after-dinner drinks; interest in Martin had waned. Nevertheless, I would need to take fairly urgent action to help our friend before he either passed out or caused a further disturbance.

I began, "Right, Martin. It's time for bed. Have you got your key?" He rummaged through his pockets without success, and then announced triumphantly, "I've left it in the room!"

"Come on, we'll get a duplicate from the desk."

Martin's response was firm and positive. "I want another drink. I've fallen through the bloody window."

"We've all had enough drink-y-poos for one day, Martin. It's time for bed."

Without further ado, Jane and I simultaneously grabbed an arm, hoisted him to his feet, and propelled him towards the door with a view to removing him from the scene as quickly as possible. However, our good intentions were somewhat thwarted by Martin's lurching gait and by his insistence on benignly acknowledging all the curious stares we encountered en route.

The hotel receptionist, who had witnessed this unsteady procession from the sanctuary of his counter, was definitely not amused. By the time the embarrassed trio presented itself before him, his brow was clouded and his lips were pursed. His doleful eyes and hangdog expression could not conceal the obvious disgust with which he regarded us.

"My friend has lost his key," I began, nonchalantly pointing with my free hand to the intoxicated character suspended between Jane and me. 'My friend', whose feet were barely touching the ground, grinned inanely.

"Perhaps we could borrow a duplicate?" I suggested, smiling hopefully. Martin vigorously nodded his agreement. The señor remained impassive. The dead weight on my numb left arm signalled the inevitability of an undignified triple collapse on to the marble floor of the foyer. I pressed on, my desperation increasing. "Please Sir, señor; we just want to put him to bed."

Ignoring my plea, he moved sideways along his counter and began to shuffle a bundle of papers. It was then that Jane saved the day. Speaking with the authoritative tone that she reserves for special circumstances, she directed a verbal onslaught in the wretched fellow's own language.

Whether it was the realisation that Spanish was being spoken with such fluency or whether it was the reference to the manager's likely involvement, we shall never know. "Si, si, señora...si...si...si, si señora." Undoubtedly, he agreed wholeheartedly with everything she said as he handed over a key and even replied in her language, twice! "No problem, no problem."

Refusing to be excluded from the action, Martin called over his shoulder as we propelled him towards the wide staircase, "Gracias, gracias, muchas gracias..."

I cut in with, "Shut up, you fool, let's go while we're winning."

Three steps forward, two steps backwards, a wave over the banisters to a puzzled stranger, three steps forward, a trip, recovery of balance: this sums up our journey to Martin's room which, thankfully, was on the first floor. We paused at the door, propped him against the wall and, whilst I held him upright, Jane turned the key. With an expansive sweep of his arm, Martin bowed and invited us to enter with, "After you, madam. After you, sir."

Jane opened the door and was almost blown off her feet by a force-nine gale that was coming straight off the sea through the shattered window. Entering quickly and shutting the door behind us we gazed at what could have been the aftermath of a terrorist attack. We were startled by the unexpectedness of Marion's question from beneath the bedclothes.

"Is that you, Martin?" Her dutiful husband raised his forefinger to crave silence.

"Yes, dear."

"Have you been out again?"

"No, dear." The finger rose again to confirm the command.

"Yes, you have. I know you, Martin," were the last words she uttered before relapsing into her drunken stupor.

I turned my attention to the immediate problem. The cause of the accident was plain to see. Martin had left his suitcase in front of the French door and, in his helplessly inebriated condition, he had tripped over it and crashed through the window. Now, we certainly did believe it! Fortunately, the heavy curtains, lined with an anti-glare substance, were drawn, limiting his injuries to a cut wrist.

Jane helped me to remove the larger pieces of glass on to the balcony but we could do nothing about the smaller fragments: a battalion of cleaners, equipped with brushes and vacuum machines would be required for this sizeable operation.

"You will need to watch where you are treading, Martin," said Jane.

"No problem," he giggled, pointing to his feet. "I'm going to sleep in my shoes." With that, he collapsed on to the bed and we made a discreet departure, deliberately leaving all the lights burning. Finally, we hung the 'Please do not disturb' sign on the outside handle of the door.

Returning to Mrs. Parker, seated opposite, I had neither the time nor the desire to relate the Martin and Marion saga to her. However, when I mentioned Martin's family name and the prestigious school he had attended, she conceded that perhaps she had been a little hasty in drawing her conclusions. I knew that there was no hope of her admitting the misconception to her customers by retelling a more accurate version of the incident. All I could pray for was that she would cease spreading the gossip about me and that, with the passage of time, the matter would fade from memory. Bracing myself, I devoted the next ten minutes to advising her of the options open to her fifteen-year-old son and then, with great relief, I bade her good-night.

I remember wondering how many times teachers and

policemen misjudge people and their actions. I vowed to discuss this premise with my friend, D. C. Charlton, the next time he called to see me.

As for Martin and Marion, they made a subdued, white-faced appearance on the following afternoon. Clearly in a state of mild shock, they could remember little of the events of the previous day. We advised them to resolve the matter with the day receptionist before the 'señor' of the previous night came on duty.

"Assume a positive stance," I advised. " Complain about the weakness of their glass. Tell him the hotel would have been liable for compensation if you had been injured."

That evening, a box of chocolates and a bottle of wine, together with a 'thank you' card, were delivered to our room. Martin and Marion checked out early the next morning, since when we have neither seen nor heard of them. Perhaps they were discouraged from contacting us by the message Jane wrote on the greetings card we sent the following December: 'Hope you have a smashing time, this Christmas!'

CHAPTER NINE

'For he who fights and runs away
May live to fight another day;
But he who is in battle slain
Can never rise and fight again.'

Oliver Goldsmith.

"Have you ever been attacked by a parent, Adam?"

As promised, Detective Bobby Charlton had called in to give me the 'low down' (his words) on his recent deployment at Greenfield School where he had been to deal with an assault on a teacher by an irate parent. Apparently, it turned out to be not as serious as at first thought. There had been no physical violence, just a frenetic onslaught of verbal abuse by a mother who objected to the rule about dangling earrings. Like most parents, she had always applauded the strict disciplinary code of the school, that is, until her own offspring were directly affected by it.

In this case, the mother had seen a delightfully cooperative and sensible junior metamorphose into a rebellious teenager, determined to challenge any regulation that frustrated her newly-discovered womanhood. Having her ears pierced had been obligatory to the process of growing up and, as a logical consequence, the hanging of a bizarre pair of danglers through the holes in her recently mutilated ear lobes.

In such cases, parents are confronted with three choices: back up the school by resisting the child's whims; do nothing and appear weak; or, afraid to withstand their offspring's wrath, join in the complaints about the school's 'draconian' regime. Fortunately, the majority of parents support the school and I believe that those who do not, really know that they should. So, to justify their disloyalty and to allay their feelings of guilt, they pretend to be even more affronted than they are. Usually, their bravado collapses like a punctured balloon when they come face to face with real authority.

According to my visitor, this is exactly what happened at Greenfield and, as the contrite mother retreated with a promise to abide by the school's rules in the future and an undertaking not to cause any further trouble, it was decided that no official action was necessary.

"As I was saying, Adam, have you ever been attacked by a parent?"

"Not since I became a Head."

"Before, then?"

"Yes, on two occasions. The first time it happened, I hadn't even qualified as a teacher. I was on a teaching practice at a very rough school. It taught me a very early lesson."

"How do you mean?"

"Well, to always be on my guard and to strike the first blow, if it comes to that. It has stood me in good stead ever since."

My young friend could not contain his curiosity. "What happened? Were you injured?"

"Not physically, but my pride was dented. I suppose I brought it upon myself. I had given my attacker's son a good thwack earlier that day. The annoying thing was that I was only there because I had specifically requested a placement at that particular school."

By my friend's demeanour, it was clear that he was eagerly awaiting an explanation so I decided to treat him to the full story. I began, "I entered the teaching profession with the zeal and ideals of a missionary. I was determined to use my talents to the full, to make the greatest possible impact that an individual can on the wretched lives of the disadvantaged. Accordingly, I sought experience in what is known as an educational priority area school where I would be sure to come into contact with life's losers. Perhaps I wasn't ready for it although, on balance, I think I did well. I received a good report at the end of my stay there."

Bobby was impatient. "How did it happen - the assault? Where was the school?"

"One thing at a time." I started at the beginning.

"The school was in a mining village in Yorkshire - quite an

experience! It was a really depressing place to grow up. Apart from going down the pit for a living, there were practically no job opportunities for the lads. This seemed to foster a defeatist atmosphere in the school. With a few notable exceptions, I saw very few signs of ambition to climb out of the humble situation into which they had been born.

It was a landscape of terraced houses, pigeon lofts and allotments. The general ambition was to own the fastest racing bird or to grow the largest vegetable marrow for display at the annual show. Oh, I almost forgot, the supreme aspiration was to breed a champion greyhound so that they could pocket the prize money as well as the infrequent returns from betting, a pursuit that invariably benefited the bookmaker rather than the punter.

Mind you, the men did adhere to a certain code of moral behaviour. In particular, although only a handful of them attended the local chapel, the whole male population had adopted a unique, if bizarre, method of observing the Sabbath. The underlying maxim was to avoid being seen to do business on Sundays. As this was the day when the majority spent time at their allotments reaping the fruits of their labours, this self-imposed regulation caused a problem every time they wanted to sell a lettuce or a pound of sprouts. One day, a bright spark hit upon a solution, which was quickly accepted as the norm.

'If it wasn't Sunday, how much would you charge for a cauliflower?'

'If it wasn't Sunday, thirty pence.'

'If it wasn't Sunday, I'd give you fifty pence for two.'

'All right, if it wasn't Sunday, pick yourself a couple from that bed.'

'If it wasn't Sunday, have you got change for a pound?'

Of course, every family did not own an allotment, or even a garden for that matter, as an attractive young lady teacher who had recently joined the staff discovered. At least a couple of times a week, she had been delighted to find bunches of flowers waiting on her desk, brought by an adoring eleven-year-old boy. On meeting his mother and father at a Parents' evening, she remarked, 'You must have a lovely garden, judging by the flowers that Peter brings for me.'

Bewilderment was evident on both their faces. 'But we don't have a garden, we live in a high-rise flat!' ventured the father, clearly assuming that it was a case of mistaken identity. On investigation, it transpired that Peter's quickest route to school was a short cut through the local cemetery and he had decided that the beautiful blooms left there would be more appreciated by the living than the dead!"

Bobby interrupted – he had heard enough of my pointless anecdotes. "Yes, thank you, Adam. I get the picture. But couldn't the kids have joined the Forces or applied to the Police or Fire Service?" He would have been a good careers adviser!

"They could have...but I didn't see any evidence of anyone trying. They tended to mistrust authority and their lack of social skills, coupled with their appalling speech, severely handicapped them. As I said, there were exceptions: the very bright ones went on to university and tended to make their lives away from the coalfields."

"I'm surprised you volunteered to teach in such a dreadful place. I suppose chaos reigned throughout."

"Believe it or not, it didn't. Both the Head and his deputy enjoyed perfect control so that it was relatively easy for the staff, and for me, to go about the business of teaching. I don't think it was an accident that, in their different ways, both were extremely unconventional. In the Head's case, it was contrived; I'm not so sure about the Deputy."

"How do you mean?"

"Well, the Head was an odd-ball in all respects, ranging from his eccentric code of dress to his outlandish behaviour. He still wore the clothes associated with the nineteen hundreds: black jacket, pin-stripe trousers, bow-tie or cravat and, occasionally, a winged stiff collar. The kids, and indeed their mums and dads, had come to accept his unusual sartorial preferences (if they knew what that meant) but they were clearly in awe of this potential madman. These sentiments were fuelled by certain bizarre practices which he was wont to engage in."

"Like what?"

"Let's take assembly, for instance. It was rumoured that he had adopted the same stratagem to ensure order from the day he had first taken morning prayers some twenty-six years earlier. The arrangement was for the pupils to file into the hall accompanied by the soft strains of a popular classical piece of music. In front of them they would see the closed stage curtains, brightly patterned with lines and loops which were intended to engage the children's interest. At a given moment, a spot-light beam would be trained on the centre of the stage where the curtains met and as the volume of the music increased to a crescendo, the curtains would slowly part to reveal the maverick Head, resplendent in academic gown, ready to administer to his flock."

"You're joking!"

"As true as I'm here, he did. Not surprisingly, among the teaching profession, he acquired the nickname of the 'Spotlight Head'."

"And was his Deputy as daft as he was?"

"Bobby, he wasn't daft, to use your word. He was firmly in control; rarely did he even have to raise his voice.

His Deputy was a different kettle of fish. I don't think she set out to be outrageous; she just could not help it. She was the tiniest teacher that I have ever seen: less than five feet and her bowed legs didn't help! The lasting memory I cherish of her is taking the whole school for hymn practice every Friday morning. When assembly was finished, the Head would leave the platform, handing over to her the congregated school. Then, rather than step up on to the open stage (I think she was conscious of her bowed legs), she would have a chair placed beside the piano and, whilst everyone froze in silent anticipation of a possible mishap, she would grasp the back of the chair and, using the rungs as a ladder, she would climb up until she was standing on the seat. Three sharp taps on the piano lid would wake us all from our state of semi-hypnosis and the lusty rendering of 'O Worship the King' would burst forth."

"This is unbelievable, Adam."

"I know. You will be pleased to learn that, in all my years of teaching, I have never again met anyone slightly resembling either of them."

"That's reassuring, anyway. Now, before I interrupted you, what were you saying about the funny way the children spoke?"

"Well, to begin with, some kids' accents were so broad, they were unintelligible. Generally, speech was littered with a mixture of mispronounced words and colloquialisms that were like a foreign language to anyone who had not grown up in the neighbourhood. Let me ask you this: does the word 'laiking' mean anything to you?"

I paused to allow my visitor to ponder. "Is to do with swimming or fishing - things you do in a lake?"

"Strangely enough, it can be, but not because of the water or lake connection. No, basically it refers to either 'playing' or, more widely, 'not working', 'enjoying leisure'." I went on, " I'll give you another example, which is perhaps even more confusing. In that part of the country, to say, 'It were real' means 'It was very good' or 'The experience was extremely enjoyable'." Bobby's bewildered expression did not alter. "Mispronunciation was even more common than the use of local slang. 'Coil' was 'coal', 'scoil' was 'school' and, even more baffling, the flat 'a' sound covered innumerable eventualities. Most people in England pronounce 'water' as 'worter' and 'watch' as 'wotch'. In that area of my native county, 'water' was 'watter' (as in 'patter') and 'watch' rhymed with 'patch'. I have a poignant memory of the mispronunciation of 'watch'. I still alternate between shuddering and smiling when I think about it."

"Shuddering and smiling?"

"Yes, I smile at the amusing incident it conjures up but I shudder when I think of what happened to me shortly afterwards." Any fears I may have had about boring my visitor were dispelled as he leaned forward eagerly, obviously keen to hear more. So I continued. "It all happened one glorious summer's evening on the cricket field of the miners' welfare. A local man, who had played several times for the Yorkshire Second Eleven, was conducting a series of coaching sessions for the youth of the village. As two of the teachers at my practice school were assisting him, I volunteered and went along to help. The incident, which still makes me laugh, involved the local propensity for mispronunciation - in this case, saying 'watch' as if it rhymed with 'patch'.

The professional was coaching the art of batting. Each aspiring player was allowed about ten minutes in the nets. My two colleagues were employed as bowlers whilst the coach positioned himself a couple of yards to the side of the wicket, on the outside of the net, from where he could comment on the various batsmen's style and technique.

Eventually, it was the turn of a powerfully built raw-boned young miner. He strode majestically to the crease. Devoid of the traditional garb, he sported a collarless shirt with a spotted handkerchief knotted round his neck, brown corduroy trousers tied with string below the knees and steel-capped working boots. Judging by the way he treated the first three balls he received, it was apparent that, in spite of refusing the offer of pads and gloves, the lad was in 'cracking' form. One ball after another was dispatched like a bullet from a gun, whistling through the air and over the distant boundary. The third one even cleared the roof of the pavilion.

In spite of this obvious success, the professional coach was not happy with the stance adopted by Len Hutton's would-be successor. Unable to condone any further denigration of the noble art of batsmanship, he yelled at the heretic, 'Watch thee feet! Watch thee feet!'

After what seemed to be an interminable period of silence, he was rendered speechless by the young cricketer's telling response, 'Aye, and thee watch t'bloody ball!' "

I don't think that Detective Charlton appreciated the rough-hewn brutal humour displayed by the relatively uneducated young man because, without showing any reaction, he enquired, "And what is it that makes you shudder?"

"Well, that brings me back to my reason for mentioning the cricket field in the first place. It was there that I was attacked by an angry father. It arose out of a fracas on the school playground that same afternoon, when I had intervened to rescue my future attacker's son from a beating he was receiving from the school first team goalkeeper. According to the crowd of onlookers, the recipient was a nasty piece of work who deserved all he got. Nevertheless, I considered it my duty to stop the fight, which I did by pulling the goalkeeper away and by fixing his arms in a 'full nelson'. This enabled the victim to scramble to his feet whereupon, half sobbing, half panting, he rushed at his opponent, who was still in my judo hold, and kicked him violently in the crotch.

My response was both quick and decisive. Without considering the consequences, I grabbed the perpetrator of the cowardly act, shook him violently and then, as he turned to flee, I struck him a hard blow across the shoulders, which caught him off balance and knocked him to the floor. When he scrambled to his feet for a second time and called over his shoulder, 'I'll bring me father up to thee', I did not anticipate that the threat would be carried out with such promptness...and certainly not on the field at the miners' welfare.

The man-mountain came upon me when it was my turn to relieve one of the bowlers by sending down a few overs of my off spin. 'Come here, Firestone, or whatever they call thee. I'll treat thee to lay a finger on my bairn!' was the gist of his opening statement, which was delivered concurrently with the grasping of my shirt collar in a vice-like grip. From the outset I realised that I was at a serious disadvantage. He was bigger than me, stronger than me and, I suspect, a better fighter. My attempts to rescue my throat from the tattooed iron bands which he called arms were futile. I'm sure he would have strangled me if my two colleagues had not moved smartly to my aid, each grasping an arm to restrain him."

"Were you not frightened?"

"Very, in fact, terrified is a more accurate description of my state. To compound matters, I was almost suffocated by the stench of stale tobacco combined with the unpleasant odour of an unwashed body. But I survived! Thankfully, my physical shape was maintained but my dignity was offended and I did wonder if my loss of face would lessen my standing among the pupils when I next reported for duty.

I need not have worried. It transpired that my attacker was the head of a problem family who had recently moved into the neighbourhood. The man was an exception in that he was a long-distance lorry driver, not a miner - in the eyes of the villagers, a foreigner. Afterwards, if anything, the kids warmed towards me as if to distance themselves from the assault. For myself, I was careful to keep my hands under control; I could not afford another embarrassing confrontation. However, I resolved to be always ready to act decisively should I be unfortunate enough to be the subject of an attack at any time in the future."

"Didn't you sue him? There must have been plenty of witnesses."

"Of course there were, but I didn't. I suppose I felt that I had brought the problem upon myself. I was more concerned with cooling it down than adding fuel to the fire. I decided to count it as experience."

"You mean, to be on your guard in case of any assaults in the future?"

"I suppose so, yes."

"And surely enough, it happened again."

"Yes, one day, many years later, I was confronted by a parent who had come to school in a very belligerent frame of mind. There was no doubt that he intended to assault me; indeed, he certainly would have done, had I not acted positively and decisively. By that time, of course, I had a dozen years of hard experience under my belt and I was Deputy-Head of the school. I could not afford to be humiliated - I had too much to lose. In that educational establishment, it was essential to present a strong and powerful image at all times."

"So you battered him before he could touch you?"

"Not as such, but I did treat him to a modicum of aggression."

"Come on, Adam. Cut out the fancy words. What really happened?"

"Well, first of all, you must realise that the school was on an estate that had been populated originally by the clearance of inner-city slums. Unemployment was well above the national average and, sadly, few parents recognised the value of education. 'Brass' was of over-riding importance to them, perhaps because they did not have much of it, and a direct way of acquiring some was to send their kids to work at the earliest opportunity. The majority could hardly wait for their offspring to attain the age of leaving; meanwhile, the compulsion of school attendance had to be tolerated. However, there was no compulsion to cooperate with the school."

Bobby understood the point that I was making. "So few parents showed any interest in their children's progress."

"Exactly, it seemed to me that their only motivation for visiting the school was to complain. Indeed, the fellow who attempted to assault me had come up to protest that I had handled his son roughly during the dinner break. I well remember the incident. It occurred whilst I was trying to say the Grace before the meal. Unlike the rest of the diners, who stood perfectly still in silence so as not to delay the dishing out of the food, young Graham persisted in prodding the boy next to him and then giggling. I had begun, 'For what we are about to receive...Graham Beal!' I started again, 'For what...Beal, I shan't tell you again! For what we are...' Would the idiot never learn? I stepped forward smartly, took him by the shoulders, and menaced him by pinning against the wall. 'Right, you can stand there and wait for your dinner until they've all finished,' which he did, sobbing with frustrated anger as the other kids showed their obvious amusement at his plight."

"So you did not hit him?"

"Definitely not, but he had been made to look foolish in front of his peers. I certainly did not expect any complaint from his home so I was taken aback when a red-faced, angry father came threatening me as I was seeing the pupils out of school at the end of the afternoon's lessons. He brushed past the lines of children filing along the corridor to the top of the stairs and, eventually face to face with me, he attempted to grab my tie. The smell of alcohol on his breath revealed where he had assembled the courage to set foot in the school. No doubt, Mrs. Beal, arms akimbo, resplendent in apron, had dispatched him on his mission a couple of hours earlier at the time Graham had run home to give an embellished version of the affair. Predictably, the master of the house had been unable to pass the 'Rose and Crown' without stopping for 'one'...or more!

Strictly in self-defence," (at this, I saw my visitor grin), "I grasped my attacker's lapels and forced him backwards along the corridor to the top of the stairs. Meanwhile, the stream of scholars continued to file down the spiral staircase. Mr. Beal, firmly held against the banister rail, miraculously underwent a change of attitude. Apparently, he was merely visiting the school to ascertain the nature and extent of his son's bad behaviour with the intention of supplementing any punishment which the school may have metered out and which, he was sure, must have been richly deserved.

I did not release my hold on him until all the children had departed. This took considerably longer than usual because, in their curiosity to see what was happening, they had curbed the lightning pace at which they normally left their place of learning. Their departure was further delayed by an accident on the staircase: two or three individuals had looked back as they descended, stumbled and caused an unholy pile-up at the bottom. Fortunately, nobody was injured.

Finally, when the two of us were alone, I carted him off to see the Head. It turned out that he had been a pupil at the school a dozen or so years earlier. He was so ashamed and embarrassed when the Head gave him a good dressing down. Then, it was the turn of all of us to be embarrassed when the wretched fellow burst into tears as the Head asked after Ethel, his wife, who had also attended the school."

Realising that my tale had ended in a bit of an anti-climax, I took pity on my patient listener. "Rather sordid hey, Bobby? We've had enough of belligerent parents for one day. Come on, I'll buy you a pint."

CHAPTER TEN

"If the law supposes that," said Mr. Bumble..."the law is an ass - a idiot."

'Oliver Twist' by Charles Dickens.

The mid-weekly Rotary lunch, once a pleasurable diversion eagerly anticipated, was suddenly transformed into an embarrassment to be dreaded. It was all because the manufacturers of motorcars insisted upon adorning their products with attractive emblems! Some, such as Rolls Royce with the Spirit of Ecstasy statuette, went even further to enhance their beautiful creations.

Of course, in blaming the carmakers exclusively for my discomfort I am being neither accurate nor fair - just frustrated. Obviously, mascots attached to the boots and bonnets of automobiles could not, by themselves, cause embarrassment to anyone. A further influence would be needed and, in my case, there was one. Somebody in Beckbridge had become a collector of car badges and was pursuing the hobby by prizing them off the town's vehicles. What is more, our enthusiast was not a proud chap - Morris Minors and Ford Pops qualified for the same treatment as Bentleys and Daimlers.

At the time this madness erupted, I had just about recovered from the problems created by the Black Hand Gang, only a few months having elapsed since it had faded into oblivion. I know that my fellow Rotarians suspected that the dreaded group were pupils of mine...and they were right, of course. Fortunately, it had been the vicar and I who had caught them red-handed so only we knew their identities. This had not prevented my friends from complaining every Wednesday, when I joined them for lunch, and I was now suffering similar jibes all because an unknown person was intent on removing every badge from every car in Beckbridge.

"Can't you exercise a bit more control, Adam?" became the normal way of greeting me as I arrived at the Club House.

"Control! I know what I'd do with 'em. I'd bring back the birch if it were left to me!" was the invariable contribution of the smallest Rotarian, a bespectacled septuagenarian, who had barely the strength to lift a birch rod, let alone administer punishment with one.

"I'll tan their back-sides if I catch anybody near my limos," interjected Ben Lomas, our Funeral Director, who in spite of his profession was normally our most cheerful and affable member.

The most severe suggestion came from Gerald, the Florist, "Me! I'd lock 'em up and feed 'em bread and water!"

Whilst I was musing on how these would-be iron disciplinarians would cope with a thousand teenagers, a brief lapse in their onslaught enabled me to say my piece, "Look fellows, there's no point in fantasising about your personal punishment for whoever it is. We've got to catch him first. Anyway, it might not be a 'he': it could be a girl who's stealing them."

"That would not surprise me one little bit. No, Sir. From what I've seen, some of the lasses at your school are worse than the lads!"

Why did they insist on assuming that all villainy emanated from Lea Grange? "Steady on, Mike, nobody knows who the culprit is. Detective Charlton and I have spent many hours on the problem and not a single clue has emerged to implicate anybody from my school." I refrained from discussing the pros and cons of locking people up...and of using thumbscrews for that matter. Yet I could have recounted a bizarre experience of only two days earlier, which had a direct connection with 'locking up' as a punishment. The incident had shocked me, a liberal, so I could not begin to imagine how it would have affected this hard-line bunch of floggers.

It had occurred when I was sitting at the Magistrates' Court, ostensibly dealing with family matters. As such, the court was held in private in a relatively small room, which had been furnished and adapted to create a relaxed and informal atmosphere. There was no dock and no witness box - just two or three tables and an adequate supply of comfortable chairs.

I was Chairman of the proceedings, supported by two lady magistrates and a professionally qualified clerk. At 11.30am., after we had adjourned a case for a social welfare report, he informed us, "Well, your Worships, that completes your business for today. The other cases listed have been agreed out of court." He followed up with the usual request, "As it is still quite early, shall I check if we can assist any of the other Benches?"

Having obtained our agreement, he hurried off whilst we retired to finish what was left of our jug of filter coffee. He soon returned, cheerfully reassuring us that we should not be detained for long. The only cases suitable for transfer were those of two fine-defaulters.

As it turned out, the small unthreatening room was an ideal setting for the first case - that of an inoffensive and terrified lady, rapidly approaching middle age I guess, who had failed to purchase a television licence. After hearing a little of her background, we quickly put an end to her ordeal by agreeing to accept a cut in her weekly payments.

It was the second fine-defaulter who gave me such a surprise, such food for thought. A tall, well-built young man of no more than twenty years, he was ushered in through a side door by a court official. Dressed in pale blue washed denims and with a clean-shaven complexion, he could have just stepped out of a bath.

I think the informality of his surroundings puzzled him initially but our clerk's opening salvo soon reminded him that he was in a court of law. "Stand up straight when you address their Worships!" Then, after getting him to confirm his name and address, the clerk announced so that all present could not fail to hear, "On the twenty-ninth of January last, you were fined eighty pounds and ordered to pay twenty-five pounds towards the costs of the court, for the offence of being drunk and disorderly in a public place. This is a total of one hundred and five pounds. Tell the magistrates why so far you have not paid even one instalment on your fine."

The accused was bracing himself to reply when the court usher entered and approached the bench. "I'm sorry to interrupt your Worships but there's a young man outside who says he's with this lad and can he come in to watch?"

Our clerk's advice was immediate. "It's a matter for yourselves: technically, it is a public court so he has the right to come in and observe the proceedings." My questioning glances at the two colleagues on either side of me were met with nods of agreement.

"Yes, please bring him in." Then, to the youth, "Come in, sit on that chair by the door...and behave yourself." He was of similar build to his friend and equally clean and tidy. I noticed that he was carrying a brown paper parcel before I returned my attention to the business in hand. I asked the clerk to elicit the usual statement of means from the defendant, at the conclusion of which I decided that the weekly figure of five pounds, which had been stipulated by the sentencing Bench, was well within his capabilities. I employed my sternest tone, "Tell us why you have not obeyed the order of the Court. You know we can send you to prison if you refuse to pay your fine." Turning to our professional adviser, I adhered strictly to court protocol and requested of him, "Learned Clerk, will you please inform this man for how long he can be locked up if he refuses to pay."

The clerk was ready with his answer, "Five days, your Worship."

I maintained the verbal assault. "You heard that! Five days for not paying. The magistrates who imposed the fine took your means into consideration when they set the amount. In my opinion, they were more than fair. You can easily afford five pounds a week. I'm sure my colleagues would not want me to even consider lowering it. They murmured in unison, "Certainly not. Indeed not."

The defendant gave his friend a rueful smile. He seemed to be deciding how to respond. By now, our clerk deemed that enough consideration had been given to the lad. His barked command shattered the silence, "Speak up man, we haven't got all day!"

Glancing once more at his mate, who immediately averted his eyes, possibly to avoid grinning, I remember thinking, the defendant heaved a deep sigh before he delivered the following surprise. Addressing us in a most courteous manner, he began, "Please Sir...and your lady Worships, I'm not being cheeky or insulting the court but I'd sooner do five days in gaol than pay the fine."

Neither my colleagues nor I had anticipated such a response. More likely, we expected him to plead for his freedom and to ask for more time to pay. The lady on my right, a successful businesswoman, was breathing deeply, no doubt seething with annoyance. I am sure she would have liked to send him down for a month or two. That would dent his self-satisfied demeanour!

"Am I hearing you correctly?" I began. "You are telling me that you don't mind going to prison?"

"That's right. Five days soon passes and when I come out the fine will be wiped off." My colleague on the left, a kind and gentle lady, was clearly upset. She whispered, "This is so sad, Adam. I'm sure he does not realise what he's letting himself in for."

I was exactly of the same mind and I lost no time in relaying our thoughts to the misguided young man, who then astounded us even further. "I don't want to appear rude but please do not worry about sending me down. I've already done two short spells. It's no problem if you can handle yourself." I noted his bulging biceps as he continued, "The food's quite good and I'm a lot better off without alcohol."

By now, his friend was moving up and down on his chair and thrusting his arm upward in the manner of a pupil in school who thinks he has the correct answer. I could sense that our clerk's strict training made him uneasy about the informality that was creeping into the proceedings but I was not concerned because the room was empty save for the three magistrates and the two lads...and the learned clerk, of course. We four court officials were undergoing the proverbial 'learning curve'.

"It's all right. Let him speak. Come forward if you want to say something."

Obviously pleased to be acknowledged, he moved quickly into a position in front of the Bench and earnestly informed us, "Please,

Sir, Dave's right. You get a cooked breakfast every morning. The cowboy breakfast is smashing!"

Dave broke in to explain, "Bacon and baked beans, you know, like on the range. The dinners are just as good - bangers and mash, fish and chips...plenty of chips."

Warming to the theme of the joys of incarceration, his friend assured us, "I'm always a lot fitter when I come out - five days off the booze and bags of weight training."

The defendant took over with, "And, don't forget, Kevin, the snooker's free, full sized tables and all."

I had heard enough. I interrupted the eulogy before Kevin could add further to their recommendation of life behind bars. "Thank you, young man. Go back to your seat and keep quiet."

Speaking, first from the left and then from the right, my colleagues respectively observed, "Oh dear," and "Disgusting," whilst our clerk fell back on the obvious, "It's a matter for yourselves."

We did not need to retire to consider our verdict. We were unanimous, if reluctant. The clerk rang for a police officer and I committed Dave to prison for five days. Kevin raised his arm again.

"Please, Sir, his mother has sent this parcel. Can I give it to him?"

"What's in it?"

"I'm not sure. A clean shirt and two pairs of under-pants, I think."

I looked quizzically at our clerk, who reassured me, "Don't worry, Sir. He will be thoroughly searched for illegal substances when he is admitted."

The two lads departed through separate exits, Dave escorted by a policewoman and Kevin unaccompanied, leaving three disillusioned magistrates to ruminate on the premise, 'the law is an ass'.

I was in no doubt that my Rotary friends would have expressed themselves in stronger terms so I decided to save the story for a more appropriate occasion. Meanwhile, I endeavoured to initiate a discussion on the forthcoming 'Roses' cricket match - anything to divert their attention from car badges!

I was becoming desperate that the culprit or culprits would never be discovered. The whole business was beginning to strain my personal relationships. In particular, I sensed that my friendship with Ben Lomas was being impaired, thus making life difficult for both of us.

He was probably the most popular member of the Club. Although his vocation was a solemn one, obliging him constantly to deal with sadness through the loss of loved ones, somehow he always managed to be cheerful. There was no doubting that he looked the part in his pristine white shirt, black jacket, and pinstriped trousers, the outfit in which he invariably appeared for lunch, yet his readiness to smile and share a joke dispelled any traces of doom and gloom that could have pervaded him. He was just as well liked by the wider community, ever to the fore with projects involving the elderly. I was always amused to see how delighted the old dears were when they were allocated a place in one of his limousines when we club members provided transport to their special events.

At the time of the car-badge trouble, as active members of the International Service Committee, Ben and I were seeing a lot of each other through our involvement with several initiatives to improve the lot of citizens of the Third World. Our Club had recently financed the installation of a water filtration unit in a village in India and we had helped to purchase a bus to be used for simple operations by a travelling eye-surgeon in Pakistan. At the conclusion of the many evening meetings devoted to the planning of these activities, the conversation would always include a reference to the latest victim of the car badge nightmare.

"It seems funny that your teachers' cars don't suffer, Adam!"

It is a commentary on my state of mind at the time that I derived a bizarre satisfaction at being able to contradict my friend. "That's how it used to be, Ben, until last Thursday morning. Eight vehicles were tampered with in the school car park. Even the logo on the minibus was taken. The geography teacher noticed it when he was loading some camping equipment. The mystery is that all our kids could be accounted for during lesson times, that morning. It must have happened at break time, which is very unlikely, unless an intruder was responsible."

By suggesting an intruder, I was conscious that Ben might think I was trying to divert attention from the school but, to his credit, he held his tongue and moved on to Rotary matters. Our most recent project had been to obtain medicines to send to less well-off countries, who were too poor to purchase them. That we were able to obtain the drugs free of charge was due to the strict British regulations relating to 'use by' dates. Arthur, the Rotarian representing pharmaceutical retailing, in other words our local chemist, had pointed out that, whilst some medicines are unfit for use after they have passed their 'use by' date, many others do not deteriorate and are safe to use without any time restrictions.

The regulations in Britain did not distinguish between safe and unsafe. They embraced every one so, at the end of each month, chemists were obliged to discard all the preparations whose time had expired. That's where we entered the equation. We obtained permission to make a monthly collection of time-expired drugs that we passed on to Arthur. His job was to separate the 'safe' ones from those which had to be discarded.

Then, at intervals, a consignment of usable drugs was dispatched to the Third World, leaving the rejected medicines to be destroyed. Obviously, this was a very serious consideration; we could not just throw them into a dustbin nor flush them down the toilet.

It was Ben Lomas, our friendly funeral director, who solved our problem. "Leave them with me and ask no questions. I'll see they are got rid of without danger to anybody."

That is as much as he would say on the subject but, as we trusted him implicitly and nobody else came up with a solution, we were happy to leave the matter in his capable hands. I knew that he conducted several cremations every week but I never voiced this nor did I ever suggest that there might be a connection between this fact and the disappearance of the unwanted drugs.

In any case, pondering on how Ben Lomas disposed of useless

medicines would not solve the mystery of the missing car badges. When the breakthrough I had been praying for eventually materialised, it manifested itself in bizarre circumstances.

About two weeks after the minibus and seven teachers' cars had been relieved of their distinct motifs, I answered a telephone call from one of our cooperative mothers. She had amassed a dozen large bags of jumble, which were cluttering up the garage, much to her husband's annoyance. In the present climate, he was not happy about having to leave his car outside and unattended overnight.

As the date of the sale was still over two weeks away, she was requesting collection as soon as possible. She pointed out that, by making a big effort to collect from all the houses on her street, she had saved us much time and trouble. Mrs. Field did not need to justify herself. She was a tireless worker on behalf of Lea Grange, having a son and daughter with us as well as nine-year-old twins to follow in a couple of years.

In those days, we were holding jumble sales at six-monthly intervals, mainly to equip our famous brass band. After each one, we managed to improve our technique and the sales developed into an effective way of supplementing our finances. We soon learned how to deal with market traders who arrived early to snap up the best bargains by asking high prices to begin with and by restricting garments to two per person. On a lighter note, we never removed our own coats, however hot it was, after a young helper's anorak was sold within a minute of his taking it off.

In line with fine-tuning our methods, we had built up a network of helpers, mainly mums, who were responsible for collecting from their friends and neighbours. When they, like Mrs. Field, were ready with a load, we would dispatch the physical education staff in the school minibus to relieve them of their bulging sacks.

On that particular occasion, I detected definite urgency in the good lady's tone of voice so I promised her a collection promptly at the end of the school day. By a quarter past four, Paul and Robin, our cheerful gym instructors, were in her garage loading the bags and by half past four they were knocking on my door with a remarkable tale to tell.

They had returned to school with not a dozen but with fourteen sacks, twelve of which were full to the brim with pots, pans, coats, trousers, and all kinds of bric-a-brac. However, it was the other two bags that were of more interest to them...and to me!

"Get a load of these, Headmaster!" was Robin's opening gambit as each teacher placed the bag he was holding on to my desk. I was conscious of their intense gaze, eagerly anticipating my reaction when I looked inside, not that I needed to because the clattering of the contents had already given the game away.

"Good gracious me!" (or words to that effect) I exclaimed. Before me gleamed the missing car badges of Beckbridge. My two colleagues began rummaging in the sacks, no doubt seeking a mascot they could recognise.

"Leave them be for the moment, fellows." I was already assessing the serious implications both for the Fields and for Lea Grange. "This requires very careful consideration. Sit down for a minute while I think." We looked at each other in silence for a while as I thought about poor Mrs. Field and how she must be feeling. "How did she react when you found this lot?" They exchanged sheepish glances.

"To be frank with you, Headmaster, Mrs. Field doesn't know that we've found them."

Paul intervened to explain, "It's my fault, I was poking around in the cupboards whilst Robin was loading. They were hidden under a pile of rolled up carpet. I really shouldn't have been looking."

Robin took over, all reassurance. "The lady doesn't suspect a thing. After she opened the garage for us, she disappeared; left us to carry on. We just peeped the horn and she waved to us through the kitchen window as we left."

"We do have a problem, though," said Paul.

"We certainly have...a big problem," I agreed.

"No, I mean finding the badges is bad enough but have you forgotten that their Freddy is in France on the twin-town exchange?"

"I bet that's why he hid the badges under the carpets," added Robin.

I made a decision! "Right, Freddy is due back on Saturday. Obviously, we shall have to report this to the police but I must tell his parents first. By the way, there's no need for you two to hang on. Oh, and well done."

I decided to wait an hour or so before I contacted the Fields in order to be sure that Father would be home from work. It was going to be one of the most difficult meetings I had ever called. Meanwhile, over a cup of tea, I considered how best to break the dreadful news. I must be as direct as possible yet I must endeavour to minimise the shock. Even more to the point, I pondered on how the law would deal with Freddy. He had never been in trouble before but it would be difficult to mitigate such serious misconduct. The damage he had caused to the vehicles would not be forgiven.

At exactly 6.15pm. I telephoned. Mr. Field lifted the receiver almost before it rang, apparently having entered the house at that very moment. I detected that he was a little irritable as many men are before they have imbibed their welcoming drink, whether it be tea, coffee or something stronger.

"If you really must see us tonight, can you get up here as soon as possible, please," was how he agreed to my visit. As I drove the short distance to their lovely home, I wondered if I should have let them eat before I dropped my bombshell. On reflection, it was better to confront the problem head on, without delay.

"Come in, Mr. Firestone, to what do we owe this pleasant surprise?" A dramatic change of mood - he must be on to his second gin and tonic!

"May we sit down a moment, please? I've got some news that will give you a bit of a shock."

Mrs. Field was immediately at his elbow. "Something has happened to Freddy?"

"No, Freddy is quite safe. No one has been injured. Look, please can we sit down somewhere: I have got something serious to tell you."

Etiquette took over from curiosity as Father stepped aside to let his wife lead into the dining room.

"Drink?"

"Please, whiskey and water...about half and half." I took a generous sip, then plunged. I omitted the bit about Paul rummaging in the garage, letting them assume that the ill-fated sacks were among the pile of jumble.

Maurice Field had not qualified as a legal executive by accident. "How do you know that those two bags were not brought in with the other jumble?" I cursed myself for not being completely frank at the outset. Yet I still prevaricated.

"Well, I don't." Then, "Yes, I do. My teachers told me that they were separate, well away from the main pile...hidden under some old carpet. It was whilst they were checking to be sure that they had got everything that they came across them."

"Is this true, Mabel? Did you leave the teachers alone in our garage?"

"Well, yes. They are our kids' teachers. They're supposed to be trustworthy, you know." I controlled my urge to react to that as she turned to me and enquired, "Mr. Firestone, do you suspect Freddy?"

I swallowed another mouthful. I was extremely uncomfortable. "It's not my place to suspect anybody. I certainly would not have believed it of Freddy. I still don't believe he would do such a thing." More silence as the tension increased. Mother dabbed tears from her eyes, Father's legal brain was in overdrive.

"What do you intend to do? How are you going to play this?"

I remember thinking that resorting to euphemism would not extricate us from this mess. "There's only one thing I can do. I shall have to report it to the police."

"Oh no!" sobbed Mother. By now she was in floods of tears and shaking uncontrollably.

Her husband moved to comfort her. Over his shoulder, playing on my sympathy, he implored me, "Mr. Firestone, you can see how upset my wife is. Can we discuss this in the morning before you submit your report? Allow us time to accustom ourselves, to prepare ourselves. Who knows, we might come up with an explanation that doesn't involve Freddy. He's been away all week, you know...in France. It's wrong to jump to conclusions."

Extremely relieved that my burden was considerably lighter now that I had relayed the bad news, I saw no reason to refuse his proposal. Now that the culprit had been identified, the vandalism would cease. In any case, I was drained. I had no wish to prolong the agony.

"Yes, of course. Leave it till ten o'clock. Give me time to get assembly over and lessons under way."

When I departed, I left behind me two extremes: the nine-year-old twins frolicking noisily in the large garden whilst their parents were inside, desperately trying to come to terms with the cruel message I had been obliged to deliver.

The next morning, I confined assembly to the basics and was back in my study by half past nine. Almost immediately, my secretary was announcing the one person I did not want to see. My visitor was Detective Constable Charlton.

"Come in, Bobby, I'm afraid I can't spare any time this morning. I'm up to the eyes."

"Not to worry, Adam," he replied. "What I want to see you about can wait. I'll pop in tomorrow if I'm passing." As he was leaving, my phone rang. It was the sergeant at the police station asking if Bobby was with us. I handed him the instrument.

"Good Lord, I'll get over there straight away." As he handed back the receiver, he explained, "A Mr. Field has reported his twin sons missing. They didn't sleep in their beds last night. There's a garbled message about a note. Sorry, I must dash!"

"I'll come with you, if you don't mind. I think I might have something to do with this." Then, in answer to his puzzled frown, "You'll see what I mean when we get there. Come on, we'll go in your car."

As we entered the front door past a uniformed constable, I didn't know what I expected to find. Certainly, I was not prepared for Mrs. Field's verbal assault. Addressing anyone and everyone within earshot, she blurted out, "He's to blame! If he hadn't called last night, this would not have happened."

I was lost for words. Bobby glanced enquiringly in my direction as Father handed me a note, obviously written by a child:

'Dear dad
It were not Fred
sorry mum'

Bobby read it over my shoulder. "Will somebody please tell me what this is all about?"

Mrs. Field had regressed into tears and her husband was doing his best to comfort her. I took responsibility and, as briefly as possible, I outlined the events of the previous sixteen hours, from when Paul and Robin discovered the badges. Mr. Field provided the reason for their offsprings' disappearance. Apparently, when they had come in from the garden, he had explained why Mum was upset and told them not to worry, as he would clear the matter up in the morning. He assured them that Freddy would not be involved.

They knew only too well that Freddy was innocent and, afraid to upset their mother further, they ran away. Bobby Charlton was very reassuring. It had not been a cold night so they would not have come to any harm. Hunger would soon bring them home if the police did not find them first.

I continued this optimistic approach, pledging full support. I don't think Mr. Field meant to be cruel when he exclaimed, "I think you've done enough!" Like his wife, he was overwrought.

"Can you drop me off at school, Officer? I may be able to help," I persevered, trying to sound convincing. Back at Lea Grange, I assembled our eleven and twelve-year-olds, the age groups most likely to be friendly with the twins. Without revealing that the boys had absconded, I sought information as to their usual haunts.

The response was encouraging. As members of a gang led by one of our twelve-year-olds, they had recently made a tree house in the local woods. Another boy had heard that they had built a den in Henry Brown's dad's barn.

My attempt to relay this valuable information to the police station was to no avail as all personnel had been sent on house-to-house enquiries in case anybody had seen the twins since bedtime the night before. I was in no doubt that immediate attention was necessary - I must act at once! I really should notify the parents...but what if it turned out to be a wild goose chase? No, I would take the responsibility and organise a quick check on both locations.

I arranged for Paul's class to be taken care of so that he could let the twelve-year-old take him to the tree house whilst I telephoned Yew Tree Farm. Mrs. Brown was alone; her husband and eldest son, David, were repairing the fence in the far field.

She knew the twins from the Easter holidays when Henry was home from boarding school. Yes, she thought they had built a den in the barn. No, on second thoughts, they had not built it. Henry's dad had made it for them...out of bales of straw, she thought. You got to it through a tunnel. Sometimes they stayed in it for hours.

"Have you seen the twins recently?"

"Well no, Henry's back at school, you know."

"Would you know if they are in the den now?"

"Oh no, I don't even know where the tunnel in the bales starts. There are so many." She was thinking aloud. "I went in this morning for the eggs. There was no sign of anybody."

"Mrs. Brown, does the barn have a lock?"

"I don't think so. No, just a wooden bar we fix across to stop the doors banging if it's windy."

"From the outside?"

"Yes, of course, if it was on the inside, we would lock ourselves in."

"Are the doors open now?"

"They were this morning. Yes, they will be, it's not windy, is it?"

"Mrs. Brown, I'm sorry to have to tell you this. The twins have run away from home. I want to help their parents to get them back quickly, before something happens to them."

"Of course. Oh dear!"

"Well, there is a chance that they might be hiding in your barn…in the den. Can you fix the bar across to fasten the doors? I'll be up there with you in less than fifteen minutes."

"I don't want to do anything I shouldn't."

"Please trust me. It's better than a load of policemen coming to arrest them. Anyway, they might not be in the barn. It's just a hunch."

"All right, but be sharp about it."

The fence that was being repaired by the farmer and his son was adjacent to the road so by the time I drove into the farmyard I had acquired two passengers. The farmhouse looked different from when Susan Gregory and I had crept up to it in search of Billy, all those years ago. But, of course, we had approached it from the opposite direction.

Mrs. Brown had made a good job of securing the two large wooden doors and she was anxiously waiting at the gate. It was quickly agreed that I should keep a low profile whilst David and his father investigated the den. After all, having fashioned the tunnel through the bales, they knew the way in.

When they drew back the creaking doors, a couple of hens fluttered into the open, then silence descended. Mrs. Brown and I watched, hardly daring to breathe, as David stooped to address the gap at the foot of the bales and gently called the twins' names. It was when he threatened to crawl in to see if they were there that I heard a muffled reply. Thankfully, we had found them!

Further exchanges ensued, with David insisting that they would have to come out sooner or later, before two dishevelled youngsters, hair and clothing flecked with straw, appeared head first, one behind the other. I imagine they were relieved to be discovered as they walked sheepishly past the men and into a smiling Mrs. Brown's welcoming embrace. She was wonderful, using both her chubby arms to hug them simultaneously before shepherding them into the kitchen with a promise of lemonade - after she had tidied them up, of course.

Her husband went through to the hall from where he could be heard speaking on the telephone to their father. The boys exchanged doleful glances, and then their heads drooped a little before they tucked into bowls of cornflakes as if they had not seen any food for many hours...which, I suppose, they had not.

When their father arrived to collect them, I was still by the door, where I had positioned myself lest they harboured any ideas of another escape. He brushed past me and I was relieved that he greeted them reassuringly rather than with the anger he must have felt. On the way out, he paused by me to excuse his earlier harsh reactions and he went on to thank me profusely for my part in finding his precious sons. Obviously, Mr. Brown's call had granted me my fair share of credit.

So, much to my relief, Lea Grange was in no way implicated on that occasion. The story appeared on the front page of the local free press and, although the law protected the twins' identities, sadly for their parents and for Freddy, too many people had been involved in the search to prevent the whole population of Beckbridge from knowing who had been stealing their car badges.

CHAPTER ELEVEN

'You cannot teach a man anything. You can only enable him to learn within himself.'

Gallileo.

Ben Black was a day late in enrolling for his secondary education at Lea Grange. He never caught up.

He arrived at 10.30am. on the third of September, accompanied by his father, who explained rather than apologised for their tardiness. Apparently, the plane on which they had just returned from a two weeks' holiday in Majorca had been delayed at Palma airport; consequently, they had not reached home until the early hours of the morning.

By their demeanour, appearance and behaviour they were already conforming to the description of the family that I had received from my friend Garvin, who was Head of the Junior School where Ben had completed his primary stage of education.

"He needs very careful watching, Adam." Before I could enquire whether he meant the father or the son, Garvin continued, "And the old man's no better. He's a plausible rogue: a wheeler and dealer...not short of a bob or two, mind you...and, I must give him credit, quite generous with fund-raising. But keep your eye on Ben or he'll cause you a lot of trouble!"

The couple before me looked normal enough. The man was well dressed in a blue serge suit, collar and tie and, I remember well, very expensive looking crocodile skin shoes. More than six feet tall and of powerful build; he could have been a very impressive figure but for his greased hair and over-long sideburns.

His son was a big lad for his age but far too fat. Although decked out in a brand new uniform, he looked untidy. His lank locks were in need of a good wash and the traces of chocolate round his mouth suggested that he had either not washed his face or had started stuffing himself with sweets far too early in the morning.

"Mr. Firestone, I want you to take my boy in hand. There's a good job waiting for him in my business if he bucks his ideas up. They let him get away with far too much at Fairfield Junior. Education is not what it used to be. In my day..."

"Right, thank you, Mr. Black. I hear you. We shall do all we can. Don't expect miracles."

My visitor persisted, "He's a good ball player, could be very good if he got rid of some of that weight."

"We have an excellent programme of physical education. I'm sure we can bring out the best in him." I refrained from stating the obvious: that cutting down on his intake of chocolate would do wonders. "Now we must hand him over to his Form Tutor, get his education under way."

Mr. Black fished in the back pocket of his trousers and withdrew a wad of paper money from which he peeled a five-pound note. Thrusting it in the lad's hand, he bade him farewell with, "Here, this is for your dinner and a few sweets. I'm due in Wolverhampton at half-past eleven so I'll be off. Behave yourself. I'll be back to pick you up at home-time." Then, turning to me, "Let me know if he's any trouble. Be as hard on him as you like!"

He was gone. I heard the throttle of a powerful car as he gunned the engine whilst I turned my attention to Ben and arranged for him to meet Robin Jackson, who was his designated personal tutor. It was fortunate that Robin taught physical education: the problem of excess weight could be addressed without delay.

In fact, Mr. Black had not exaggerated about his son's ball-playing skill. The boy's prowess at table tennis was remarkable and he was equally competent with a soccer ball, only hampered by his inability to chase up and down the pitch. Nevertheless, he soon secured the goalkeeping spot in the First Year Eleven, a position he held with distinction throughout the season.

Unfortunately, his academic progress and general behaviour did not live up to his sporting achievements. Sadly, both were barely satisfactory and, towards the end of his first year with us, I was to learn that his conduct at home was even worse.

My first intimation of this was through a phone call from his father. Mrs. Jones, my secretary, announced, "Ben Black's father is on the telephone from a place called Hinckley. He needs to speak with you urgently."

"Hinckley? That's near Leicester. Put him through, please."

"Mr. Firestone, I'm devastated! I've just missed an important deal. Let me get my hands on him. I'll kill him!"

I was still silently digesting his opening salvo when he went on, "Are you there, Mr. Firestone?"

"Yes, I can hear you. Look Mr. Black, you will have to explain what is happening. Do you want me to do something for you?"

"Too bloody true, I do. I want you to grab that creature of mine and relieve him of forty quid before he spends it."

"Forty pounds?"

"Yes, forty bloody pounds. I know he's got it. I counted it out last night - seven hundred and sixty pounds, to be exact - before I went to bed. It was for some business down here. It's always cash in my trade."

While I was thinking, "I bet it is," he continued.

"Like a fool, I clinched the deal, then, when I counted out the money, it was short by forty pounds. Our Ben must have pinched it this morning while I was getting ready. I'll murder him!"

"How can you be so positive that Ben has taken it?"

"Because it's not the first time, nor the second, for that matter."

"Oh, I see. You had better leave it with me. I'll do what I can."

"I'll be back in the Valley before four. Shall I call in?"

I agreed to his request and then turned back to my two deputies, who had sat patiently waiting. "I'm afraid we shall have to put this meeting on hold. That was Ben Black's father. You probably got the gist of the message."

David James had. "He suspects Ben of stealing forty pounds?"

"Right first time. If Sarah will excuse us, you can be Doctor Watson while I demonstrate a bit of elementary detection." We were soon entering the form-room where our target was learning the rudiments of algebra.

"Please be seated, girls and boys." To the teacher, "May I?" Then, back with the pupils, I came straight to the point. "A large sum of money is missing. Until it is found, everybody is a suspect. If it does not turn up, I may have to ask you to empty your pockets." I paused to survey the class without resting on anybody in particular. I was hoping that they would think that the money was missing from school or, more to the point, I was praying that Ben would make that assumption.

"Now girls and boys, listen carefully to what I am going to say. It may be that you have brought some of your own money to school today...for a proper reason, of course, and I don't want any of that to get mixed up with what has been stolen." I paused again, for longer this time, whilst the eager, honest faces (well, nearly all honest faces) gave me their undivided attention.

"Therefore, if you have a bit more money with you than usual, tell me now so that we can clear you from any suspicion." Their young brains were working at full stretch, carefully weighing what I had said to them. Soon the predictable hand was raised.

"Yes, Ben?"

"Please, Sir, I've got thirty-two pounds on me. My dad gave it to me to buy a new pair of gym shoes."

"Right, thank you Ben. Anyone else?"

Nobody! The class began to fidget with relief. The tension was visibly receding.

"All right, Ben. Come along with me, we will sort this out straight away." David James raised his eyebrows, shook his head slowly from side to side, smiled ruefully and excused himself, whilst Ben and I withdrew to my study.

When I invited him to tell me the truth about the money, he refused to come clean until I picked up the telephone to call his mother. Realising that he would be digging a deeper hole for himself, he owned up. He had seen his father counting the cash before he went to bed the night before. He could not sleep for thinking about it and when he awoke earlier than usual, it was still on his mind. When he went downstairs, there was nobody about.

The wallet was on the hallstand. He removed eight five-pound notes and pushed them under the stand. If his father had checked the bundle and found some missing, Ben would have helped with the search and produced the notes, 'which must have fallen on the floor'.

It transpired that Father had been pushed for time that morning and when he rushed off, Ben was able to retrieve the money at his leisure. He concluded his confession by admitting to me that he had already spent eight pounds on sweets for his ever-increasing circle of friends. Then, he added, "I'm surprised he missed it - he's got plenty stashed away. He thinks more about his dogs than he does about me!"

"Dogs?" I had noticed that Mr. Black was always accompanied by a large Alsatian, which, mercifully, he left in his car when he visited Lea Grange. I did not know of any other animals.

"Yes, Janus, who goes everywhere with him and the two bitches that guard the house. He says they are better than a burglar alarm." I realised that I was drifting into dangerous waters so I did not pursue the matter further. Although I intended to leave any admonition or punishment in the hands of his parents, I felt it was my duty to prepare him for the impending disaster that was about to befall him. Unless he was prepared to show at least a trace of remorse, I feared for his safety.

Mr. Black's arrival was earlier than expected so I used the time, over a pot of tea and biscuits, to prevail upon him not to be too hard on his son. As they departed for home on that fateful afternoon, I was by no means confident that he would heed my plea.

Nevertheless, I was soon hearing rumours that Ben had turned over a new leaf. Certainly, he avoided trouble in school and my detective friend, Bobby Charlton, told me that his father had bought him a pony and arranged for him to have riding lessons at the police stables. Perhaps the career aspirations had been revised: the father's apprentice-in-waiting was now to be a policeman. One thing was certain, his knowledge and experience of law breaking would serve him well - the poacher turned gamekeeper!

The upturn did not last, yet the next episode in Ben Black's chequered career at Lea Grange should have been decisive, should have taught him a lesson once and for all. Two uncomfortable years had elapsed since the Hinckley incident and the fourteen-year-old lad's physical shape had undergone a dramatic transformation. Surplus fat having been replaced by muscle tissue, he was strong, fit, and healthy...and an even bigger nuisance than he had been when he was less mobile. He had acquired the reputation of being a bully but we were never able to prove this and deal with him appropriately.

At about five o'clock one evening, when I was thinking about clearing my desk for the day, Robin Jackson attired in tracksuit appeared at my door.

"Ben Black is lying down in the medical room. I think you should know that I've clobbered him. He'll be OK."

"Clobbered him?"

"Punched him - in the gym."

"Accidentally, of course?" I prayed.

"Not really. I had to. It was him or me!"

In answer to my questioning grimace, Robin described the incident. Several boys had remained behind for the boxing club, Ben among them. It was his first attendance and, Robin noted, the first time for three of his cronies. After the usual bout of coaching, it was his custom to allow selected pairs to don the gloves and box two shortened rounds in a makeshift ring. On occasion, he would agree to spar with one of the group, really to let the boy try to land a punch on him. Robin had attained a high standard in his youth, reaching the semi-finals of the British Schools' Championship. He was still very agile and he could sway, weave, and dodge to keep out of range.

Although Ben was a newcomer, he had requested the opportunity to box with his teacher. It was then that Robin should have been aware of the hazardous situation that was developing, a situation that was bound to slip out of control. Indeed, there had been several tell-tale signals earlier, during the coaching session.

For instance, Ben had not needed to be taught how to punch.

The skilful way he took the weight from his left leg to obtain full power for his practised 'straight left' indicated that either he was a 'natural' or that he had received instruction in the noble art from some other source. When the lad went to work on the punch-bag, the regular members of the club visibly winced. Perhaps the strongest clue to Ben's previous experience of pugilism was in the way that he exhaled noisily every time he practised a punch...and the fact that his well-worn boxing boots obviously had not been purchased recently.

Robin did recall sensing an unusually hostile atmosphere emanating from the lad's chums as the two gladiators addressed each other prior to the bout. Immediately after it commenced, he realised that his full attention would be needed to contain his opponent's vicious onslaughts.

Ben's crude aggression worried Robin who, on several occasions, had to supplement his evasive and defensive tactics with a light jab, just to keep his young attacker at a safe distance. These clips and jabs, gentle as they were, only served to increase the ferocity of the assaults. He was only just managing to keep out of trouble when the designated timekeeper rattled a tin and shouted, "Stop, end of round." Robin moved backwards out of range but, instead of doing likewise, his savage opponent, tears of anger streaming down his face, rushed forward and attempted to fell his teacher with a mighty right uppercut.

Robin insisted that he could not remember clearly what followed. He assumed that his instinct had taken over as he swayed sideways and dispatched a left hook, which halted Ben in his tracks. However he was adamant that, at that juncture, his head took over from his instinct for he did not follow up with the obligatory right cross. It had been unnecessary - the single punch had ended the contest.

I hurried along to the medical room where I found Ben nursing a bruised ego, nothing more. He assured me that he was all right, even claiming that he had enjoyed the bout. No, he did not want a lift home and he would rather that we did not mention the episode to his father. Subsequently, I was sorry to hear that he had failed to turn up at any further meetings of the boxing club. Robin did not share my regret!

Ben's next serious mishap, only a few months later, again involved the paternal parent. I learned the full story by assembling bits and pieces of information that came my way at various times from various directions, not always in chronological order. I became involved in the matter when Mr. Black came up to complain that some of his son's friends were encouraging him to steal money from home.

"It's hard to accept that you've got a 'bent' son, Mr. Firestone. You have kids of your own. How would you feel?" Whilst I was trying to formulate a suitable reply, he went on, "He's been mixing with bad company recently. You've got some rogues here, you know!"

Ignoring his initial question, I addressed the main purpose of his visit. "You say Ben has been stealing money from you and his mother, and you think that other boys have been making him do so?"

This presented my visitor with a dilemma. He was desperate to find an excuse for the boy's relapse into his old ways but he was loath to suggest that his son was so weak that he could not withstand the pressure of his peers. Had he forgotten that I knew about the Hinckley episode? In any case, I was in absolutely no doubt that Ben was a tough guy with a mind of his own. I had no intention of allowing his father to attribute the blame for his son's recent lapse to a group of my pupils, none of whom was capable of forcing Ben to do anything against his will.

As a gesture, I agreed to speak to the three boys he had named and, in fact, it was from them that I obtained most of my information. Apparently, for a number of years, Mr. Black had been storing very large sums of money in his wardrobe, which he kept locked at all times. ("My business deals are always done in cash so I have to have some of the 'readies' by me at all times.") I now understood why he kept three Rottweillers, or were they Alsatians?

Ben had known of this treasure chest for some time and he had long directed his mind to finding a way into it. He would only take a small amount; not enough to be missed but sufficient to generously supplement his weekly allowance.

He had discussed the challenge with his three close buddies and, eventually, they had arrived at a solution: pivot the cupboard away from the wall, unscrew the back panel, help yourself to a few notes, screw it back and re-position the wardrobe. Simple, and nobody would be any the wiser as long as he did not become too greedy.

In fact, Ben had successfully employed this foolproof system for more than a year before he was undone by a very unfortunate coincidence. The account so far, had been related by the three wide-eyed boys, each in turn leaning forward eagerly to take over when another's momentum started to wane.

Meanwhile, whilst my mind was striving to keep abreast of the revelations, I was concurrently trying to decide who was the more 'bent' - Mr. Black for evading his responsibilities to the inland revenue or his son for helping himself to a share of the tax-free bonanza.

Returning to the stroke of ill luck that heralded the end of our hero's supply of extra funds, the bulk of my information came straight from the horses' mouths - from those who were in attendance when the bubble burst.

It occurred one Friday night in Mr. Lee Wong's Chinese Palace, a restaurant situated in a small town seven miles away, which was linked to Beckbridge by a regular train service. Over the previous five or six weeks, Ben (or rather Mr. Black, unknowingly) had financed the outing of the foursome and treated them to a slap-up dinner rounded off by a generous tip.

I anticipated the part about Mr. Black turning up at the same eating-place one night, before the narrator had reached that stage of the story. He was being shown to a table with his two companions when he happened upon the four diners. That he did not create a fuss suggests that his guests were valuable customers although he did pause to ask how his son had come to be there. At that moment, Mr. Wong came over to greet Mr. Black as a new customer who could be persuaded to become a regular. If Mr. Wong had left it at that, Ben may have been able to conjure up a plausible explanation but Mr. Wong did not leave it there. He went on to praise the four 'young gentlemen', whom he considered to be among his best clients. Even then, there may have been a way out for Ben but as the four departed, the elder Black could be seen in deep conversation with their Chinese host. They did not need two guesses to work out the likely subject of his enquiries.

I can only assume what went on between Ben and his father when they eventually met at home later that night. Nobody was there to witness the boy's admission of guilt or the desperate attempt to mitigate his crime by laying the blame on "greedy, bullying and over-demanding friends".

As far as I was concerned it was a matter to be resolved within the Black household. I took no further action. I suppose that I did fall short in my civic duty by failing to notify the Inland Revenue authorities that there was a 'bent' tax-evader in Beckbridge!

Ben left Lea Grange as soon as he attained the statutory leaving age of sixteen years. It was just as well that he did not require any academic qualifications to join his father in the wheeling and dealing business because he did not obtain any. Not one person attempted to persuade him to stay on with us - disruptive influences are unwelcome in any place of learning!

Several months later, I was not surprised to hear that he was no longer employed in the family business although my source of information was an unlikely one.

One day, as I was sitting in the magistrates' assembly room, prior to entering court for the morning session, I noticed a familiar surname on the list of cases. A Mr. Eugene Black had been charged with a motoring offence. The address given was Laburnum Grove, which was plumb in the middle of my school's catchment area.

"I may know one of our clients," I said to Mark, our clerk for the day.

"Which case number?"

"Four, case number four, Eugene Black - charged with no insurance."

"It isn't a problem, Sir. He's pleading guilty so it's not

essential for us to have three magistrates. If you do recognise him, just move over to the side and let Mr. Smith take the chair for that case."

My colleague, David Smith enquired, "Why has Mr. Black bothered to appear? He could have pleaded guilty by post."

Mark explained, "He must attend because he is due for disqualification. I think he intends to ask you to suspend the disqualification on the grounds that a driving licence is essential for him to conduct his business."

It transpired that Mr. Black already had four current endorsements on his licence, all for speeding. Under normal circumstances, he would have been banned on the previous occasion that he was before the court but, after being subjected to a strong and eloquent plea, the Bench had agreed to give him a final chance. His advocate had convinced the magistrates that the loss of his licence would be likely to take away his livelihood.

As he was already on a final warning, one would conclude that he was wasting both his own and the court's time by even asking for further consideration. However, he genuinely believed that the circumstances surrounding the 'no insurance' charge were so unusual that it was worth a try.

When his case was called and he appeared, we recognised each other simultaneously. I think he was relieved to see me vacate the Chair and take a seat in the wings. On the other hand, he may have been disappointed on the grounds that I, as an acquaintance, might have acted with lenience towards him. I'm afraid that Mr. Black and I operated under different rules.

As I observed the proceedings, I found the situation fascinating. It was like attending a theatrical performance!

Usher: "Call Eugene Black."

The defendant came forward and was shepherded into the witness box.

Clerk: "Are you Eugene Black of twenty-four Laburnum Grove?"

Mr. Black: "Yes, Sir, that's me."

Clerk: "You are charged that, on the eighth of July, you were in charge of a motor on the public highway, which was not covered by a current insurance policy."

Mr. Black (loudly): "It had no engine in it." Then, looking round at the public, "Good gracious me!"

Clerk: "Please do not interrupt. You will be given the opportunity to state your case at the appropriate time. Now, how do you plead to the charge: guilty or not guilty?"

Eugene Black looked across towards his lawyer, a well-known 'mouthpiece' for the less salubrious members of local society, who answered his quizzical glance with a silently mouthed, "Guilty."

Mr. Black: "I'm pleading guilty...but I'm not happy about it."

His advocate got to his feet and coughed to indicate that he had something to say.

Advocate: "What my client means is that the circumstances of this case are extremely unfortunate and, I hope the Bench may accept, out of his control."

Clerk: "Thank you." Turning to face Eugene, "Mr. Black, you can leave the witness box. I suggest you sit by your counsel. Now, listen to the prosecution's statement of facts."

Prosecutor: "At 7.30pm. on the eighth of July, P.C. Jones was on motor patrol. On a public highway, namely Laburnum Grove, he came upon a motor vehicle parked at the front of number twenty-four. The front offside tyre was deflated and the car was in a generally poor state. In view of this, P.C. Jones called at the house to investigate further. He discovered that the vehicle was not covered by insurance."

Mr. Black: "It had no engine, either. I've been shopped by that bitch next door. She hides behind the curtains, spying on us!"

Clerk: "Mr. Black, you will not help yourself by constantly interrupting the proceedings. Leave the talking to your lawyer."

Advocate: "Thank you, learned clerk." He then aimed his words at my two colleagues. "Your Worships, my client is the victim of a very unfortunate succession of events. He fully accepts that the car should not have been on the road. On the day in question, he was in Durham - he travels a lot in his business - and he did not arrive home until after nine o'clock. He is prepared to swear that the car was on his drive when he set out that morning. There's no way that he could control what happened when he was so far away. He has already told you that it has no engine. There was no chance of it being driven. Now, you may be wondering how it came to be on the public highway. The answer is simple but very distressing for Mr. Black, who is an upstanding member of our town trying to chisel" (a most unfortunate choice of word, I thought) "out a living in this difficult economic climate. I'll tell you the answer, Your Worships: my client's seventeen-year-old son, Bert, and a friend pushed the car off the drive."

Mr. Black: "Ben."

Advocate: "Ben?"

Mr. Black: "Yes, Ben...you said Bert. My boy's name is Ben."

"Advocate: I'm sorry, Your Worships. In any case, it was...er...Ben who pushed it on to the road to make room for his friend's car on my client's drive. They wanted to check the electrics for a fault. You know how keen on cars the young lads of today are."

Clerk: "You are not suggesting that Mr. Black has no liability?"

Advocate: "Oh no, of course not, indeed not, I know my law. What I am asking Their Worships to consider is that no reasonable person could hold him responsible, given all the circumstances. In view of this, he has asked me to plead for a further suspension of his disqualification."

Clerk: "Thank you. Right, Mr. Black, please return to the witness box." Eugene shrugged as his lawyer whispered something in his ear, and then slowly rose, no doubt dreading the worst, as the clerk continued. "You are asking for your disqualification to be waived a second time. You are aware that it should have been activated on your last appearance before the court - four endorsable offences already, and all for speeding!"

Mr. Black (not helping his case by grinning at the public gallery): "I can't afford to hang about in my business."

Advocate (anxious to repair the damage): "What my client

means to say is that, although time is of the essence in his kind of work, he was clearly wrong to be careless about watching his speed, for which he unequivocally apologises to the Court, and he deeply regrets any inconvenience this has caused."

Clerk: "Thank you. Now Mr. Black, is there anything else before Their Worships retire to consider your application?"

The lawyer looked quizzically at the defendant, who shrugged his shoulders before shaking his head.

Advocate: "No, I think that is all, learned clerk. Perhaps I may just remind the Bench that Mr. Black was miles away, somewhere between Durham and Beckbridge, when the offence took place."

With that he took his seat, then immediately rose, as did all present, whilst my two colleagues retired to decide Mr. Black's fate. I deliberately remained in the courtroom so that he would be in no doubt that I had not influenced their decision.

We were not kept waiting long before the usher commanded all to "Please rise" at the re-entry of the two magistrates. In delivering their considered decision, the stand-in Chairman, David Smith, managed to be both sympathetic yet unambiguous.

In the first place they had found the offence proven: there could be no doubt that Mr. Eugene Black was guilty of permitting a vehicle to be on the public highway without insurance cover. Furthermore, he had already used up his 'last chance' in connection with a previous misdemeanour and, in our Court, 'final' really did mean 'final'! However, having considered all the factors surrounding the offence, they both felt a degree of sympathy for the defendant and, in view of this, they were prepared to mitigate what should have been, in normal circumstances, a relatively severe punishment. Do I sound as pompous as this when I pronounce from the Chair? A modicum of humility would not be out of place!

There was more. The two wise men had decided that a six-week ban, supplemented by a fairly hefty fine, would be both appropriate and fair. Such a period would enable Mr. Black to arrange to be driven by a stand-in.

To his credit, Eugene received the verdict in respectful silence. Before the two of us went our separate ways, there was just enough time for me to walk over and shake his hand.

Through gritted teeth he vowed, “That lad of mine again. Will he never learn? I promise, I’ll swing for him one day!”

CHAPTER TWELVE

'Please to remember
The fifth of November,
Gunpowder treason and plot;
We know no reason
Why gunpowder treason
Should ever be forgot.'

Traditional Nursery Rhyme.

Eugene Black may have been a wheeler and dealer, even a plausible rogue, but he could not be labelled a nuisance. True, he had felt the need to seek our help on numerous occasions but only once did he attempt to attribute his son's behaviour problems to the influence of the school. That was when he suggested that the boy's friends were responsible for his stealing money from home. Even then, he quickly backtracked when he realised that such accusations cast aspersions on his son's strength of will.

Generally, all the parents of Beckbridge were a delight to deal with: appreciative, supportive, and always respectful. During my headship of Lea Grange, I can only think of one father who caused me anything more than mild anxiety. This is a remarkable statistic considering the thousands of parents with whom I dealt.

Denis Forrest's father was normally one of the most affable and helpful members of the parents' association yet, under certain circumstances, he became an acute embarrassment and, at times, a veritable 'enfant terrible'. By profession, Cedric was an accountant and he bore all the hallmarks that are unfairly attributed to that worthy calling. Well-mannered, sober, boring, clean-shaven and always ready with his silver-plated pen, one would have thought that he dare not say boo to a goose. But observe him, clad in deer-stalker cap and waterproof trousers, running up and down the touch-line watching his son play centre-forward for the school team and you would see before you a different creature - more demon than human being. As well as portraying Lea Grange in a poor light, his verbal assaults on visiting referees were nothing short of incitements to violence. His behaviour was at its worst when Denis was being given a hard time by the opposing centre-half.

"Did you see that, ref? Rubbish! Put your specs on. Are you bloody blind?" were a selection of his milder comments, invariably accompanied by appeals to fellow spectators and rude gestures clearly aimed at the referee. Eventually, Keith Walker, our first team coach, decided that he'd had enough.

"He behaves himself when you are watching. When you are not there, his behaviour is completely unacceptable."

"Leave it with me, Keith. I'll sort him out," I said with misplaced confidence.

In fact, sorting him out was much more difficult than I would have imagined. I was embarrassed at having to admonish a grown man, a professional man to boot, about his conduct, which could only be described as childish.

I'm ashamed to admit that I took the easy way out by resorting to euphemisms such as, "Now, Cedric, you must not allow your keen support for the school team to raise your blood pressure" or "You know, you will affect Denis's performance if you expect too much of him."

It was all to no avail. Of course, he agreed with me as we sipped a glass of sherry in the comfort of my study after a meeting of the parents' association but, on the next occasion he heard a referee's whistle, he reverted to his wild state, totally out of control.

By then, my situation had worsened because I had assured Keith that I had spoken sternly to Cedric. I had insisted on an undertaking as to his future conduct so there would be no more trouble from him! Now that he had broken his promise, my reputation was in danger.

So I tried again with Cedric, much more forcibly and sticking strictly to the point this time. I even ventured to suggest that he should stay away from matches if coming to watch Denis had such a dramatic effect on him. Again, in the cold light of day and well away from the football field, he was completely acquiescent.

"I know exactly what you mean, Headmaster. That's why my wife refuses to come with me!"

Influenced by such a self-deprecating admission, I deferred my original decision, which was to ban him from all future games. In retrospect, I wish that I had done so at that stage because, mainly due to him, our next home fixture was a disaster. It was a cup match, drawn against a prestigious school, whose keen supporters had needed four buses to transport them the twenty-mile journey to Beckbridge. By the time they arrived, well over a hundred 'hurrah Henries' decked out in brightly coloured scarves and tweed jackets were in the mood for a bout of good-humoured banter. They were not expecting to meet anyone like Cedric Forrest!

The match was evenly contested, one of the most thrilling to be played on our field. Perhaps that was why everyone, including Bill Brown our school keeper, did not notice the intruders, who swept through the dressing rooms, stealing watches, money and other valuables without discriminating between home team and visitors' pockets.

Meanwhile, on the school field, Cedric Forrest could have been at a different match from the referee and all the other spectators, irrespective of whom they were supporting. According to him, his son was denied a penalty four times. On each succeeding occasion, Cedric's appeals increased in volume and set new parameters in the art of verbal abuse.

There was no place for us, Lea Grange's conventional supporters, to hide; pupils, parents, teachers, and I all had to endure the embarrassment caused by the bizarre behaviour of a frustrated accountant. With a minute to go and no goals recorded, I was deciding on how I would order our problem father to stay away from the replay when disaster struck - our opponents scored a perfectly executed goal assuring them of a place in the next round at our expense.

Our people sportingly joined in the applause, which resounded round the ground only for it to be brutally interrupted by Cedric's foul words as he ran on to the pitch to berate the referee. Mercifully, he did not attempt to lay a finger on him although, on second thoughts, perhaps it's a pity that he did not because the man in black would have taught him a salutary lesson if size and muscle development count for anything.

Before we had been able to apologise to our visitors over the obligatory cocoa and rock buns, a loud and discordant chorus of distressed human voices had announced the theft of the valuables. I dreaded to imagine what they must have been thinking of us. It would take a decade to restore Lea Grange's reputation in their part of the county.

Fortunately, Detective Charlton and two colleagues immediately recovered all the watches and most of the money. It transpired that the same two window cleaners, who had been operating on the Lake Distict housing estate, had perpetrated the thefts. For weeks, the two had been the subject of surveillance by an unmarked police patrol, who now had caught them 'red-handed' as they drove out of the school grounds.

There was still the problem of Cedric Forrest to be dealt with. By the time the fuss about the stolen goods had died down, he was nowhere to be seen. I rejected the idea of making any further attempts to coax him with friendly words. Instead, I took the bull by the horns and sent him an official letter in which I forbade his attendance at any future sporting events. He replied by resigning from the committee of the parents' association. He did not have the decency to apologise for all the trouble his lack of control had caused. I thought it was all very, very sad.

Still, balanced against the antics of Cedric Forrest, I enjoyed numerous exchanges with parents that were of a positive nature on which I look back with satisfaction. Soon after taking up my appointment at Lea Grange, I could have been faced with a terrible situation if thirteen-year-old Ian Hudson's father had reacted as many parents in his position would have done.

The problem arose in a physics lesson one Friday afternoon. It had rained incessantly all day and, as all teachers know, such conditions seem to have an adverse effect on children's behaviour...and, in this respect, Friday afternoons are much worse than Monday mornings! The teacher in charge did not help the situation. Graham Thorp's undoubted enthusiasm was not matched by the requisite degree of control. I was aware that he was not completely at ease with his groups but he did seem to be getting better week-by-week. I was confident that, one day, he would develop into a more than useful member of his profession.

My optimism was based on his conscientious approach to his work: he would go to any lengths to interest his students. Within a few months of his joining the staff, he had persuaded me to purchase an astronomical telescope and he was unstinting in the amount of his own time he gave to tracking the heavens with groups of bewitched kids.

I don't think that he could understand, let alone accept, why the same boys who shared those fascinating evenings, could be such a nuisance to him in formal lessons. He felt that he deserved better; it seemed unfair to him that more experienced teachers, who put themselves out far less for their classes, did not have to endure the type of misbehaviour that came his way.

At times, this sense of frustration caused him to lose his temper and this is what happened on that rainy afternoon. Ian Hudson and his friend had chosen to sit behind a tall fume cupboard where they would be out of sight of the teacher's demonstration table. Leaning towards each other, their heads almost level with the bench and giggling uncontrollably, they were undoubtedly up to mischief when Graham suddenly appeared behind them.

On the spur of the moment and with no thought of the consequences, Graham pushed their heads together, an action he immediately regretted because, just before the impact, Ian Hudson, possibly sensing danger, half turned and took the full force of his friend's hard skull on his two front teeth. The result was inevitable: the left incisor snapped and Ian was minus one half of a front tooth.

By five o'clock the same evening, I was endeavouring to explain the 'accident' to his father, George, who had responded immediately to my urgent call. Having anticipated a most uncomfortable interview, I felt the outcome was far less painful than I could have hoped.

"Mr. Firestone, what is done is done. I know our Ian's no angel but cracking his teeth is going a bit too far!"

I resisted the temptation to correct him by pointing out that only one tooth had been broken. It was not something to treat lightly.

"I can assure you that it was an accident, Mr. Hudson, a most unfortunate accident, I agree. The teacher is devastated. He really loves kids; he wouldn't harm a fly.

"That won't do much for our Ian's tooth, will it?"

"Well no, not as such...but after I rang you I did some more phoning One of my Rotary friends is a dentist who specialises in cosmetic work. Did you know that most film stars have their perfectly good teeth capped to improve their smiles? Well, anyway, I have explained the situation to him and he has offered to have a look at Ian at half-past nine tomorrow morning. He says that it sounds like a routine job." I added, "Your Ian will look like Sean Connery when it's finished."

"You've got a persuasive way with you, Mr. Firestone, if you don't mind me saying." He pondered a while, then continued, "I don't want to cause you any trouble, you've made a big difference since you came to Lea Grange but that young teacher, Thorp or whatever his name is, deserves a good roasting."

I jumped in, "Mr. Hudson, let us do our best for Ian. Let Mr. Cox see him tomorrow morning. We'll cover the fee...and, I promise that I will have words with Mr. Thorp, although nothing I say will make him feel worse than he already does." With that, we parted on good terms. The dental exercise was a complete success; not surprisingly, Graham Thorp and I were greatly relieved.

They say that lightning does not strike twice in the same place. It did in Ian Hudson's life, much too soon after the dental debacle for my liking because, once again, the school was implicated. This was frustrating because we were in no way to blame: the mishap occurred well away from Lea Grange and well out of school hours. What is more, Ian was only there because he had volunteered his help.

For several years, the Beckbridge Rotary Club had organised a charity bonfire on Guy Fawkes' Night. From modest beginnings, it had developed into quite a large event, efficient publicity having played no small part in this growth. Apart from producing posters for display in shop windows, we printed handbills for posting through the local letter boxes. This task was performed by volunteers from among our students who operated in groups under the leadership of a Rotarian, his responsibility being to transport his team to their designated area and take care of them.

As luck would have it, the hapless Ian Hudson, in his eagerness to ensure that his bills were pushed well through, took to feeding them in with his outstretched fingers. 'Feeding' is the correct description of his actions because, at one large detached residence, that's exactly how the bulldog waiting on the inside of the letter box interpreted the situation. Ian was badly bitten, his broken skin shedding a profusion of blood, which made things look even worse than they were. His team leader rushed him to the hospital casualty department where he received six stitches and a tetanus injection. Again, his father's reaction was unbelievably pragmatic. "These things happen, Mr. Firestone. Your friend could not have done any more. It will teach the lad to be more careful where he puts his fingers!"

I was beginning to view George Hudson in the same light as the patron saint of England; after all, he had been given the same name. I certainly felt that I was in his debt: as the saying goes, I owed him at least one favour, if not two! My chance to repay him occurred sooner than I could have imagined.

During the last few days leading up to the Guy Fawkes extravaganza, final preparations were put in hand. Stalls were erected and decorated, potatoes, treacle toffee and, of course, the fireworks were ordered and the essential task of building the bonfire was completed. Two days before the event, an extra-ordinary meeting of the Rotary Club was held to allocate duties such as ticket-collecting, car-parking and stall-minding.

It was this meeting that was so abruptly interrupted by Detective Charlton with the 'bad' news that our precious bonfire had been prematurely ignited and that it was already too far gone to be extinguished. The irrelevant 'good' news was that he had caught the culprits, two ten-year-old boys, one of whom happened to be George Hudson's youngest son, Georgie. My Rotarian friends were prompt with their judgements.

"They need a good hiding!"

"I'd give 'em a taste of the birch!"

"The little devils should be locked away!"

"Schools are far too easy, nowadays!"

I wondered how long I should have to wait before somebody put the blame on the teaching profession. As a father, I felt a deep sorrow for George senior; I would have spanked young Georgie there and then if I could have got my hands on him.

I really wanted to help old George. "Look fellows, we must carry on with the bonfire somehow. Too many tickets have been sold for us to let this stop us. We can't cancel it at this late stage."

"And where can we produce another bonfire from. It's taken weeks to collect all that wood. Those kids are criminals!"

I did my best to appear confident. "Leave it to me. I guarantee another bonfire will be ready in time. Trust me, it will be all right on the night."

My good friend, Ben Lomas supported me. "That's good enough for me. If Adam can get us another bonfire, let him get on with it. At least the Guy did not go up in flames." Then, after a pause, "We have still got one haven't we?"

"Yes, of course, it's safe in my stock room at school. Now you chaps finish allocating the jobs...and don't be late on Thursday. I want to go with the detective to see the boys' families. I know both sets of parents; they will be devastated."

Seated in the police car next to Bobby, I began, "Have you reported this yet?"

"What are you getting at, Adam? What's going on in that mind of yours?"

"I'll put my cards on the table. The Hudson family has had more than its share of bad luck, some of it through the fault of my school yet they have never made a fuss about it."

"So you want me to help you to repay a debt by failing to do my duty?"

"Come off it, Bobby, you know I would not ask that of you. Think, what will happen to two ten-year-olds if you report them."

"They will be made to attend at the Station with their parents and the sergeant will administer a caution. He'll scare the living daylights out of them!"

"Exactly, and I'm sure that nobody would disagree with that course of action. Well, under these special circumstances, can't you go round to their homes, play hell with them, give them a caution and then report that the matter has been resolved to your satisfaction."

"I suppose that there is provision for me to do that, although I have never proceeded in that way myself."

"There's always got to be a first time. How about it? You will not be breaking any rules."

"OK, Adam, I'll do it, but I can't guarantee that the sergeant won't call them in after he has read my report."

"We shall have to risk that."

In fact, Bobby's action was deemed to be sufficient and the matter was completed to everybody's relief. I was left to carry out my undertaking to produce a bonfire in a day and a half, a promise I had made in the knowledge that there was always a pile of broken furniture in a local authority dump about two miles away.

A polite telephone call obtained permission for me to relieve the store of anything that was 'beyond repair', a judgement with which I was to be trusted. Little did the equipment clerk realise that I was desperate to obtain a truckload of any materials that would burn! The man in charge of the store was almost as pleased to be rid of some sixty broken chairs as he was to see the back of two pre-First World War teachers' desks, the ones complete with platform to elevate the master high above his cowering charges.

"I've warned the Office a dozen times about 'them' monstrosities, Mr. Firestone. They're both riddled with woodworm. It'll eat into everything...if it hasn't already done so!"

"Well, you can stop worrying now. Just give us a hand with

those old packing cases and we'll be out of your way," I said, warming his palm with a five-pound note.

A fellow Rotarian had laid on transport. The following night was dry, crisp and starry, and much to my relief, the gala bonfire was a rip-roaring success.

I shall always be grateful to George Hudson. As for little Georgie, he turned out well and followed in his elder brother's footsteps to a school of mining in the West Country before obtaining a lucrative position in a diamond mine in South Africa.

CHAPTER THIRTEEN

'And Moses' father-in-law said unto him, "The thing thou doest is not good. Thou wilt surely wear away, both thou and this people that is with thee: for this thing is too heavy for thee; thou art not able to perform it thyself alone...Hearken now unto my voice, I will give thee counsel...provide out of the people able men...and they shall bear the burden with thee." '

Exodus 18 xvii-xxvi

Heads of large schools are faced with the same problem that confronted Moses when he led the Israelites out of bondage: they have taken on a job that is too big for one person alone to perform. Whether or not they succeed in their mammoth task depends on how effectively they utilise the staff resources that are available to them.

"You're a lucky devil, Adam. You've got a really good set of teachers!" is a comment that is directed at me with tedious regularity. On this occasion, Detective Bobby Charlton was the speaker.

"Yes, I am blessed with a wonderful staff...but it's not all down to luck, you know."

"How do you mean? If it is not luck, what is it?"

"It's a long story, Bobby. If you can spare an hour or two, I'll explain. Of course, I'm proud of my staff; I'm proud of the teaching profession in general. Most teachers are able, conscientious, and dedicated but, like all other groups in society, some teachers, only a few I'm pleased to say, are not up to the task. It is the way their difficulties are tackled that affects their chances of survival as well as having a direct bearing on the morale and performance of the rest of the staff."

"You mean, sack anybody who can't cope as a warning to

those who want to scrounge?"

"No, Bobby, I do not mean that! In my experience, there are not any scroungers in the teaching profession. It is more a matter of dealing with people who are not suited to the job. Fundamentally, the best way to ensure that a school is staffed with competent teachers is by being ultra-cautious when new members are being recruited. It is especially important to go over references with a fine toothcomb. Of course, it is also essential to keep a paternal eye on those already in post."

"In other words, check the goods before you buy and then set up a system of quality control."

"That is it in a nutshell."

Bobby persisted, "But how do you discard a product that is not up to standard?"

"That's one of the biggest problems that confronts Heads. The easiest way is to not appoint sub-standard people in the first place. However, occasionally selection procedures misfire and, of course, a new Head has had no influence on how the staff he inherited were appointed. Let us look at three cases involving different teachers: it will illustrate what I mean. To hide their identities, let us call them Tom, Dick and Harry Grubb.

Tom's case is a perfect example of how taking care to study references can prevent the appointment of an unsuitable person. He was a candidate for the post of Deputy-Head when Sarah Roberts was appointed. In actual fact, he got as far as the interview before the warning bells began to ring. On the face of it, a cursory look at his references had suggested that he would be ideal for the job but, when I met him at the pre-interview lunch, there was something about him that aroused my suspicions. An immediate telephone call to his principal referee, supplemented by persistent and incisive questioning, revealed that, four years previously, he had been suspected of misconduct in a boys' school in Africa, although nothing definite had been proven.

This information, together with my instinctive feelings about him, persuaded me that I could not take any chances with him. As it happened, both Sarah and David James performed better at the interview than he did so I did not have to take any action to resist his appointment...but I was prepared to do so if the circumstances had demanded it. Of course, Tom is not the only person who has fallen at the first hurdle."

Bobby's interjection showed that he was warming to the theme. "Obviously, it is better not to appoint someone than to have to dismiss them at a later stage."

"Exactly."

"That makes sense in any walk of life."

"True, mind you, when interviews take place at Lea Grange, some of the staff derive a macabre pleasure out of forecasting whom I shall deem to be unsuitable, and why. One of the funniest observations as to why a young man and a young lady were both unsuccessful applicants for a history post was, 'His hair's too long and her skirt's too short.' "

"Did you really turn them down for those reasons, Adam?"

"No, of course not...but the fellow's unkempt appearance did not help him, particularly as we were trying to encourage higher standards among the boys. Anyway, let's move on to Dick. His was a completely different case in that he managed to pass my initial screening although he did receive unfair assistance to enable him to do so."

"Unfair assistance? In what way?"

"To put it bluntly, I was conned by people who should have behaved far more responsibly. At that time, we were desperately in need of an additional English teacher so we had posted an advert in the evening newspaper. This had prompted an approach from a local teacher-training establishment to my Head of English, who then immediately informed me that he had just had a call from Fairhaven College about our vacancy.

'They are the people who sent us Robbie Smith,' he said.

'He's excellent,' I enthused.

'Absolutely,' he replied. 'Well, they say that this chap is every bit as good as Robbie, one of their best students, yet, to their surprise, he has not managed to land a job. His problem is that he goes to pieces in formal interviews but he's supposed to be dynamite in front of a class.'

Pragmatism took control of me. 'Have we had any other applications?'

'Not a dickey-bird, so can we arrange to see him?'

'We've no choice. Let's have him in before somebody else snaps him up.'

We quickly discovered that the report from the college was only partially correct; to be exact, it was true to the power of a half! It was spot on in respect of his interview performance, which was woeful, but, as we had been warned, we were prepared for that. It was his teaching ability that we were concerned about. Because he was so strongly recommended and because his referees had been accurate about his interview behaviour and, sadly, because there were no other applicants, we took a chance on him.

It was the fifty percent of the report that related to his performance in front of a class that was way off the mark. In short, we soon discovered that he was utterly inept; he had not the first idea of how to control a group of children and the kids were quick to realise this. I, and indeed many other members of staff, continually had to quieten his classes if only to enable lessons in adjacent rooms to proceed. From the first day that I saw him walking up the drive towards the school building, I suspected that we had erred in appointing him. It was as if he was trying to avoid being seen: head turned to the left with eyes fixed on the ground a yard in front of him, shoulders drooping and a visible lack of purpose in his step.

I spent many hours counselling him as did my friend, Len Benson, the local adviser; all to no avail. To be fair to him, I believe he did all he was capable of doing to help himself: always early for lessons, work prepared with meticulous care, up-to-date with marking and tidy in appearance. The problem was that he froze as soon as a class entered his room; children quickly respond to such signals and show no mercy."

"It must have been hell on earth for him," interrupted Bobby.

"I'm sure it was but I had to balance my human sympathy for him against the damage he was inflicting on the unfortunate members of his classes. I did not need reminding how dreadful he was but, in case I had overlooked his incompetence, I was inundated with letters and phone calls from most of the mums and dads of Beckbridge."

"Is he still with you?"

"No, after six months of trauma and a great deal of persuasion, he decided to change to librarianship; after all, books do not require much discipline! Mercifully, he obtained a post within a few weeks. Had he not decided to leave, I should have had to engineer his dismissal."

"Can you do that?"

"In theory, yes, but it can be a very complicated procedure. Then again, it can be quite simple if one is prepared to be ruthless. This is what happened in the case of Harry Grubb, my third example. He was completely different from Dick in that he had no difficulty in controlling his classes because he terrified them. The problem was that he did not teach them anything. I inherited him when I came to Lea Grange. By then, he had been on the staff for about two years during which time he had carved out for himself a very comfortable existence. He was more of an odd-job man than a teacher; delighted to undertake any task that took him away from the work he had been engaged to do. At the time, the school leaving age was being raised to sixteen and our Mr. Grubb was quick to take advantage of the various schemes that were being introduced to occupy the less academic pupils."

"You are losing me, Adam. Schemes for the less academic pupils?"

"Yes, when the statutory leaving age was changed from fifteen to sixteen, it caused a lot of resentment among many kids who were obliged to stay on for an extra year of schooling. Scores of so called educationalists saw these reluctant students as a potential source of trouble so they hurriedly rustled up schemes of work with the sole aim of containing them and thus keeping them out of mischief."

"Now you mention it, I vaguely remember some of the kids at my school being taught to service motor-bikes. It was called 'Preparation for Living'. Others were taught brick-laying and some, wall-papering...but they still seemed to get into trouble."

"Exactly, and I'll tell you why. Instead of regarding their course as a privilege, they saw it for what it was: an attempt to occupy them for the extra year that had been tagged on to their schooling. They realised that they were being treated differently from the other kids and they resented it. Anyway, we are getting away from the point. Before we return to Harry, let me just say that the 'Preparation for Life' courses in some schools were a resounding success provided that the right kind of people ran them. Harry Grubb was not the right kind of person to run anything. As the saying goes, 'he could not organise a chocolate club in a brewery' (or something like that), yet he had persuaded my predecessor to let him introduce such a course."

There were many attractions for Harry. In the first place, there was to be no exam at the end of the session so his work, or lack of it, could not be assessed objectively. Another plus as far as he was concerned was the informality of the approach so he always had a plausible excuse for not being where he should have been at any given time. I realised that his students were gaining little from him and I determined to take drastic remedial action. Whilst I was considering how to approach the problem, in particular, how I would resist the reasons he would proffer to enable him to retain his sinecure, I was presented with further cause for concern about him, in quite different circumstances.

I noticed that he had absented himself from morning assembly without first obtaining my permission. Perhaps I over-reacted but I was cross that he had taken it upon himself to stay away without clearing it with me. When I tackled him about it, his pathetic excuse made me even more annoyed.

'I've been helping Cook; she likes me to sharpen her knives.'

'In future,' I replied, 'if you want to work in the kitchen, please do so in your own time and not when you should be attending my assembly!' I thought that was the end of the matter for he was ever present at future assemblies. Almost three months had elapsed before I became aware of the significance of the knife-sharpening episode.

In the interim, I had actually warned him three times about leaving groups unsupervised whilst he went off to enjoy himself...I dread to think where. On the third occasion, the censure had been administered formally in the presence of David James. I made a note of it in the logbook and required Harry Grubb to initial it. I wanted him to be in no doubt that my patience was exhausted.

It was a telephone call from the Deputy Director of Education that elevated Harry's visits to the kitchen on to a more sinister plane than the innocuous task of sharpening knives merited. The conversation began pleasantly enough: 'Mr. Firestone, how are you? I'm sorry to be the harbinger of bad news but a rather delicate matter has surfaced concerning the good name of Lea Grange...Are you still there?'

'Yes, of course, I'm trying to think what it might be.'

'Is this a secure line? Can we speak freely? Can anyone listen in to us?'

When I had reassured him that we could not be overheard, he continued, 'We have had three anonymous letters over the last two weeks stating that two of your teachers are involved in an amorous affair, which is not only affecting their work but is the talk of the neighbourhood. Normally, we don't take notice of people who hide behind anonymity but, in this case, the matter is so serious and we think that the allegations may be true because we have been given the names of the alleged culprits. Apparently the man is married and old enough to be the girl's father.'

'It may be the talk of the neighbourhood but it's news to me!'

'That does not surprise me - the boss is usually the last to hear about such things. Anyway, the Director wants you to look into the matter. He wants it sorting out, one way or another. You can report directly back to me.' He then named the two teachers: Mr. Harry Grubb and a lovely girl whom I'll call Helen.

I sat staring ahead for some time. I was absolutely certain that no self-respecting female would give Harry a second glance let alone a beautiful young woman like Helen. On a five point scale of attraction, I would award him minus two. Of less than medium height but of more than medium weight, his efforts to conceal his ample stomach failed miserably: the excess flab merely protruded over his tightened belt. True, his flannel trousers were well creased but in the wrong places and, like the rest of his clothing, cried out for the attention of a dry cleaner. I wondered whether his nickname, Grubby, derived from his appearance or was a play on his surname. Yet some mischief-maker had taken the trouble to communicate slanderous remarks about him and Helen to our Chief Education Officer. Was it somebody who really hated Harry?...or Helen?...or both of them? Perhaps it was a disgruntled parent intent on stirring up trouble for me. I was at a loss to know where to begin.

When the next day dawned, my powers of detection had made no progress before the mystery took a further twist. On my return from morning assembly, my secretary met me with the news that Harry's wife had telephoned in a state of tears, complaining that one of our young teachers was trying to steal her husband. The postman had just delivered an unsigned letter to that effect. She was sure it was true because, over the past two months, he had been going out on his own without telling her where to or who with. Realising that Harry would be met with an angry tirade on his arrival home, I decided to sort out the problem straight away. He was furious that his wife had contacted the school about his 'private business'. I allowed him time to express his anger and calm down before I sought his help in identifying the letter-writer. After what seemed an age of puffing and blowing, exhaling excess breaths from his seething body and wiping sweat from his ruddy countenance, he astounded me by declaring, 'I know who it is. Don't worry, there won't be any more trouble from that madam!'

He refused to reveal the name of the person whom he suspected but he went to great lengths to assure me that I should have no further difficulty from 'that source'. I decided to withhold the news about the letters to the Director until he had got over the shock of the one sent to his wife. He swore that he had never been involved with any of his female colleagues although on one evening, about a month previously, he had taken Helen in his hatchback to pick up a new dining set she had ordered from a cash and carry warehouse."

Bobby had been hanging on to every word. “Did you believe him...about the furniture, I mean? Did you suspect them of having an affair?”

“Definitely not but there was hardly time for me to make up my mind when the saga moved on a stage further.” I continued with the tale.

“The same afternoon, I had received an urgent request from cook to discuss the plight of Cindy, one of her assistants, who had collapsed in a distressed state in her office. I hurried over to the kitchen where I was met by the anxious cook and a sobbing young woman. When I entered the office, the heaving and sobbing ceased for long enough to allow a tear-stained face, smudged with mascara, to ascertain who had joined her, before the wailing resumed even more purposefully. Eventually, she calmed down enough to give us an explanation. ‘Bloody Grubb’ had ambushed her as she was about to leave for home after her shift and he had left her in no doubt what he thought about her and her letter to his spouse. ‘And to think I have given him everything a woman can give a man! I hate him!’

I was still decoding her message when I realised that Cook wanted me to step outside. An imperceptible movement of her eyes for my benefit accompanied the explanation she gave to Cindy. ‘I’ll make us all a nice cup of tea. Mr. Firestone, can you give me a hand?’ Then, back to the distressed young woman, ‘There, there, love, you’ll be all right. We shan’t be more than a few minutes, then we’ll see about cleaning you up so you can get off home.’

Once outside, looking very embarrassed, she explained. ‘I’m sorry, I’ve known about their affair for some time. Mr. Grubb used to come in regularly, offering to sharpen knives, but he spent most of the time whispering to Cindy. I kept meaning to tell you but I let it pass when he ended the visits two or three weeks ago. One of my ladies says that they’ve stopped seeing each other out of school but that Cindy thinks he’s switched to going out with one of the teachers. She’s all eaten up about it. Personally, I’m glad it’s finished. I never liked him coming in to my kitchen. Those fingernails, filthy...and that hair always needs a good wash. Ugh!’

She shuddered before dropping another bombshell, 'My ladies won't tell me what the two of them were up to when I was off with pleurisy!'

This latest development added a new dimension to the 'Grubby' saga. His conduct had been far more outrageous than I could have dreamed. If I was to learn the whole truth, I must strike while the iron was hot: a few searching questions whilst Cindy was still smouldering with resentment. I spoke briefly to Cook. 'Forget the tea for the moment. Come into the office and listen carefully. I may need you as a witness.'

My companion broke the ice. 'How are we now, Cindy, love? Mr. Grubb should not have upset her like that, Mr. Firestone.'

I adopted her approach. 'Indeed not, Cook. I shall speak to him about it.'

Cindy was in no doubt how I should handle her disloyal lover. 'He needs more than a talking to. He deserves a bloody good hiding and if I were a man, I'd give him one.'

I gambled, 'You only wrote the letters to get back at him.'

'I did! How dare he ditch me for that young bitch? He's no angel, you know! Your Mister posh Harry Grubb is no bloody angel!'

Cook joined in. 'He really has upset you love, hasn't he?'

'You'd be more than upset if you knew what him and me did in your office.' She then gave us a graphic account of their joint misconduct. I won't bore you with it, Bobby!"

My detective friend did not press for the lurid details but he did comment that my method of eliciting the facts would not be acceptable in any police station in the United Kingdom. I merely observed that I had the good name of the school to consider and I continued my narrative.

"Realising only too well that I should not get another opportunity to learn the whole truth about Mr. Harry Grubb's unprofessional activities, I had probed a little further. It was now or never. 'Cindy, why did you suspect him of having an affair with Helen?'

'Because he's moved in with her, hasn't he!' (An assertion

rather than a question.) 'I saw them in his van with a load of furniture.' She broke into tears again. 'He keeps a mattress in the back. I don't know what my Benny will say.'

I did not need Cook's disapproving glance to persuade me to wrap up my interrogation at that point. I distinctly remember thinking that my role in life was to educate the coming generation; I was not qualified to give marriage guidance to the previous one! In any case, I had heard enough and I was fearful of the trouble that lay ahead. By that time, school had closed for the day and Harry Grubb had departed with his usual haste. The only doubt in my mind was whether he should be banished from the teaching profession *sine die* or whether it would be sufficient for him to be removed from his post at Lea Grange.

The following morning, I did not need to send for him. When I arrived, he was waiting at my door trying to appear calm but obviously agitated as he hopped from one foot to the other. 'I just thought you'd like to know that I've sorted it out. My wife understands and there won't be any more letters.'

'You'd better come in and sit down, Mr. Grubb. You are quite right. There will not be any more letters; four are quite enough.'

He paled before stammering, 'Four?'

I hope that I did not enjoying the spectacle of seeing this incorrigible rogue squirm. 'Yes, the one to your wife and three to the Chief Education Officer.'

'The Director?'

'The very man.'

'In Preston?'

'Yes, his Deputy wants to see you this morning at ten-thirty in my study.'

I was a mere observer at the execution, just a fly on the wall. I admit to feeling sorry for Harry even though he thoroughly deserved the treatment he received. When he entered, our visitor rose and shook his hand.

'This is a bad business, Mr. Grubb.'

'Yes, Sir, I would not want to embarrass Mr. Firestone or the school.'

'Quite, the Director knows that. He's a very fair man, the Director.' Harry's demeanour communicated his relief which, sadly for him, was to be temporary. The Assistant continued, 'An exceedingly fair man is our Director.' He allowed the three of us time to ruminate on what a very fair man we all worked for. Harry nodded in the manner of a man who knew only too well; whether his nods were in agreement or pure optimism, I shall never know. When our visitor considered that we had mused long enough, he went on, 'Mr. Grubb, you are in local politics, I believe?' Harry was still nodding his approval of the previous assertion. This new approach not only startled him, it posed quite a problem. How could the Chief Education Officer's reputation for fair dealing have any bearing on his own private pursuits? His eyes strayed to a point somewhere on the ceiling above my head, whilst he considered his reply.

'Mr. Grubb?'

'Well, yes. I lost my council seat at the last election but I'm still a member of the party.'

'Mm. I suppose you are well acquainted with most of the school governors?'

'Oh yes. I count many of them among my best friends.' He saw no harm in letting him know that he had a bit of clout.

'Precisely, the Director wants to be fair about this. He does not see any reason for the governors to be involved.'

Harry must have thought he was home and dry. 'I agree. It was only...'

'Please allow me to finish, Mr. Grubb. As I was saying, the Chief does not want to trouble the governors so no more will be said about the matter...as long as you are not on the staff of Lea Grange after the summer holidays.'

Harry's comfortable smile was replaced by a look of complete dismay as his brain analysed the significance of what he had just heard. We were into the second week of July; September was only a few weeks away. As the hatchet man had not briefed me on how he would deal with Harry, I was equally taken aback. The cat had played with the mouse before it gobbled it up!

Harry was the first to break the silence. 'You're sacking me, aren't you?'

'Indeed not, nothing of the kind. I want to make that abundantly clear to both you and Mr. Firestone. The Chief wants to be fair to all concerned. (Not again!) He does not see the need for a formal investigation...the embarrassment and all that. Of course, you are entitled to your rights, Mr. Grubb. If that's how you would prefer to proceed, please let Mr. Firestone know.' Turning to me, 'It can be arranged quite easily, is that not so?'

'You stink. The whole lot of you,' was how Harry summed up the situation as he rose to depart without pausing to excuse himself. There was no more to be said. I had just witnessed Machiavelli at his best: the end justifying the means. I told myself that Harry's remaining on our staff would have been out of the question therefore there was no point in becoming squeamish about the way his departure was engineered."

I am sure that Bobby did not approve of the official's methods. "What happened? Did he leave you?"

"Oh yes. He served out the last two weeks of the term, and then slipped away quietly. He got a job selling insurance. He won't dare to apply back into teaching. He'd be stuck if he could not name me as a referee and I certainly would not be prepared to 'con' anybody in the way that I was misled about Dick."

It took me a while to decipher Bobby's final gem. "So the best way to get rid of a misfit is not to appoint him in the first place!"

CHAPTER FOURTEEN

'What is this life if, full of care,
We have no time to stand and stare?'

William Henry Davies.

These opening lines from one of my favourite poems aptly illustrate the situation faced by members of the teaching profession. They care tenderly for the well-being of their pupils, they care desperately about the development of their pupils yet, if they are to achieve any success in meeting the inexorable needs of their pupils, they will have no time to stand, let alone time to stare! The demands associated with the education of our youth are relentless; if teachers do not remain on top of their job, the job will surely get on top of them.

"But what about the long holidays?" asked Jim Stevens, the town clerk, whom I had encountered in the snug of the Blue Boar in Oldchapel. I deliberately avoid using the verb 'met' because this would suggest that our coming together was a prior arrangement, which, on that occasion, it was not. This pleasant surprise and the glowing log fire, which mine host Lionel had built in response to an early autumn chill, plus the added presence of Henry White, our solicitor, made the meeting all the more enjoyable.

It was not my normal practice to call in to a public house on the way home from school but, as Jane had taken our sons to an Advent Concert by the Halle Orchestra in Manchester, I had decided to indulge myself with a pint of beer and a bowl of Lionel's traditional Lancashire hot pot.

When Jim framed his question, I was conscious that he was winding me up like one of the unfortunate salmon that fell victim to him and Henry on those tranquil Sunday afternoons by the River Lune at Kirkby Lonsdale. However, as I had anticipated spending a couple of hours with nothing but my own company, I gladly took the bait. After all, neither Jim nor his genial companion was capable of real nastiness; it was merely his perverted way of using Friday evening to begin his weekend relaxation.

I listened as he went on, “At least twelve weeks every year - surely that leaves plenty of time for leisure?”

I responded to this old chestnut in my usual way by delivering a two-pronged salvo: in the first place, without adequate breaks, almost all teachers would crack under the strain and secondly, as well as preventing the inevitable collapse, regular breaks provide the time to rebuild the stamina which is essential for future survival.

I usually refrain from citing also the time given voluntarily by many teachers to educational visits at home and abroad but, as I had plenty of time to spare, I weighed in with it on this occasion. “Contrary to the perception of the general public, these are many times more demanding on human resilience than the day to day working under the umbrella of the school environment...and the strains and stresses are not confined to the young and inexperienced. I know! Sit back and listen while I tell you what happened to me in my first school.

‘Please, Sir, will you look after my money till we get to Skeggie?’ piped up little Alfie Edwards.

‘How much is there?’ I asked as I painstakingly counted the handful of loose change he had thrust upon me. This turned out to be a wise precaution!

‘Seven and sixpence,’ said the wide-eyed, honest-looking thirteen-year-old.

‘Just a minute, there’s only seven shillings here!’

‘Oh yes, I forgot, Sir. I’ve got a tanner down my sock.’

Not a promising beginning to a day out at the seaside. It was the late summer of 1951 so I suppose seven and sixpence in pre-decimal currency was a reasonable amount to take on the trip. The bulk of it would have been saved from his paper round, supplemented by the odd tip when he collected the money on Friday nights...and possibly the extra coppers he squeezed out of unsuspecting customers by claiming that he was short of change.

Having said all this, and even taking into consideration that the tanner down the sock was a blatant attempt to swindle me, I would not classify Alfred as a crook, just a likeable rogue.

Eventually, three charabancs were crammed with chattering children, first gear was engaged, and we were on our way to Skegness, second only to Cleethorpes as the seaside resort most frequently visited by the residents of our catchment area. In those days, good money could be earned down the pit and excursions to the east coast were favoured in preference to crossing the Pennines to Blackpool. Even so, for more than half of that day's trippers, it would be their first ever sight of the sea. That was the prime purpose of the day out; our benevolent old headmaster deemed it a 'scandal' that so many of the little devils were deprived of what we all took for granted whilst the family income was squandered supporting the local breweries and the nearby greyhound stadium.

One hundred and two excited youngsters, accompanied by six gullible teachers, were divided among the three buses. What miserable quirk of fate had decided that Frank Brown and I should be in charge of the group graced with the presence of Alfie Edwards? With hindsight, of course, I realise that it was not an accident; it was just that our more experienced colleagues had flatly refused to be responsible for what he was likely to get up to!

Frank and I had recently completed our first year of teaching in the small Yorkshire mining place and we were now considered capable of taking joint charge of the third bus. True, it was not our first school excursion; we had visited York earlier in the summer as part of the Festival of Britain celebrations. But, as teachers on probation, we had been spared any responsibility. 'Just enjoy yourselves and leave the kids to us,' was how Chalky, the organiser of the visit, had put it.

What better than the Skegness trip to afford us the chance to repay our debt but, even so, there had been no reason to allocate all the rogues to the same coach, namely ours! Still, once the doors were firmly closed, our thirty-one chattering charges were technically imprisoned, their opportunities for mischief severely curtailed. Nevertheless, after three miles or so, I decided to move

Alfie Edwards to my place next to Frank at the front so that I could have a better view of the occupants from the seat the rascal had originally selected in the middle of the back row.

Before we reached our first port of call, a roadside shop with smelly toilets, we had stopped twice: the first time so that a girl could be sick in a lay-by; the second so that the driver could threaten to turn the bus round and go back home if the 'two devils half way down the aisle stand on their seats one more time.'

As the kids poured out of the bus into the morning drizzle of the Lincolnshire Wolds, the sort of fine rain one tends to ignore only to find oneself quickly soaked to the skin, the passengers of the first two coaches were moving back to their transport. Our two earlier stops meant that we were running fifteen minutes late. Chalky, the teacher in overall charge, was guarding the entrance to the shop and his first words were music to my ears if not so well received by our party.

'Sorry, there's no time for shopping. Use the toilet, then straight back on to the coach.'

'There's nowt worth buying.' In view of Chalky's pronouncement, a straggler from the second bus relayed this piece of useless information.

Then, from his companion, 'Kiddo's been nicked for pinching!'

There was no wonder that our leader was keen to keep the occupants of our bus out of the shop, especially as the owner had agreed not to press charges so long as the stolen bar of chocolate was paid for and the 'thieving little buggers' immediately vacated his premises. Chalky was determined that the fellow's patience should not be tried further.

So we arrived at our seaside destination relatively unscathed if somewhat fraught - the kids bursting to be set free, and Frank and I in no mood to detain them. 'You've got six hours to yourselves. Remember what you have been told about keeping out of trouble and if you do need help, ask a policeman.' (Some hope!) 'Be back here by a quarter to six. The driver won't wait for any latecomers.'

Frank took over. 'One at a time, steady Brian, the sea won't run away!'

They all vanished into thin air then a little girl called Maisie Brown came running back to leave her raincoat on the bus now that the sun had appeared.

'Let's have a drink, Frank.' So began our six hours of relative peace during which, remarkably, we only encountered three of our pupils and they were well-behaved girls from Chalky's coach. When we returned to our transport at five-thirty, at least a half of our party eagerly awaited us.

'Please, Sir, Alfie Edwards has been chased by two 'fellas'!'

'From Woolworth's, Sir; he came out through the fire doors.'

'I was with him, Sir. He was nicking bags of peanuts.'

Frank was already assessing our situation. 'Did they catch him?' he enquired.

'I've no idea, Sir. I didn't hang around in case they tried to blame me.'

'Was anybody from our school caught?' I ventured. Like Frank, I was planning on how we could spirit ourselves away and avoid a whole load of trouble. As more of our party arrived in twos and threes, each group was keen to relate the saga of Alfred Edwards.

'Yes, yes, we know all about it. Hurry up and get on the bus. Sit in the seat you were given this morning. I want to see if anyone's missing,' ordered Frank, clipboard and pencil at the ready. From where I was standing all the seats seemed to be occupied yet I was not a bit surprised when he descended the steps and announced, 'Everybody present except Edwards!'

The driver had been taking a keen interest. 'I'm not waiting for anybody after six o'clock and that's definite!'

'What's the problem, Adam?' Chalky was carrying out his final check prior to departure. I explained the situation.

'Well the buses can't be delayed, that's for sure! I said we'd be back by nine o'clock and the parents will be expecting us then.' We were all quiet while he thought. 'One of you will have to stay over in Skegness. Give him another hour, then ask at the police station if any accidents have been reported. For goodness sake, don't mention Woolworth's.'

I was grateful that Frank volunteered to stay but somewhat perplexed by Chalky's response to his question, 'What shall I do if he doesn't surface by bedtime?'

'You'll just have to use your initiative.' Chalky rendered this gem of 'helpful' advice over his shoulder from the steps of the bus as he climbed aboard. Meanwhile, I was left to cope single-handedly with our group, minus its most problematic member, of course. As things turned out, compared with the outward trip, the homeward journey was relatively uneventful. Perhaps the little darlings had exhausted themselves on the roundabouts of the fun fair or maybe they had run themselves to a standstill on the miles of golden sand. More likely, they were subdued by the Alfred Edwards affair. I certainly was!

When the driver drew into the kerb by the school gates, I was not surprised that Alfie's parents were not among the couple of dozen who were waiting to be reunited with their offspring. If everybody is loved by somebody, where were all the other mums and dads? However, I was more than surprised, indeed I was shocked, when a chimney sweep's apprentice emerged unsteadily from the rear of our coach. It couldn't be...but it was! Alfred Edwards himself, in the flesh! Apart from his two white eyeballs, he was covered in grime from head to toe. He was too shaken to answer me when I enquired, in no uncertain manner, from where he had materialised. Eventually, he muttered in a laboured stammer,

'From...from...under there...From under the...b...b...bus.'

On that one occasion he was speaking the truth! Apparently, after out-running his pursuers in the back streets of Skegness, he had doubled back to the bus, hoping to slip aboard and hide. Of course he found that it was locked so he crawled beneath it in case his pursuers extended their search to our parking lot. Whilst he lay trembling with fear, he spotted the broad ledge behind the rear axle...at this point of the story he collapsed into a sobbing fit and the rest was left to my imagination. Suppose he had fainted or even fallen asleep and dropped in front of a following vehicle? What if he had mistaken a halt at a crossroad for our arrival home and been crushed as the coach moved off?

I shudder to contemplate who would have been held responsible had there been a tragic outcome to what I can now look back upon with amusement. Perhaps the lad had heeded Chalky's advice to Frank and adopted it: 'You'll just have to use your initiative!' "

Henry interrupted this narrative – it was his turn to stir the pot! Perhaps he was enjoying this unexpected entertainment, particularly as it was so early in the evening, and he feared that it was coming to an end. He need not have worried; I do not dry up when I've got a captive audience!

"Yes, Adam, but have you not chosen a most bizarre story to illustrate your point? Surely the trip to Skegness was not a typical example of what is likely to occur on an educational outing?" They both looked at each other and then at their empty glasses. I took the hint and asked Lionel to draw three more pints of the dark old ale that he always put on tap when winter approached. I was glad that my home was within walking distance and that I should not be going there by car!

"Returning to the point you have raised, Henry, that's just it! School trips are never typical. However carefully the Skegness visit had been organised, nobody in the whole wide world could have dreamed that Alfred Edwards would have insinuated himself on to a ledge underneath our coach. The moral is, whenever one is bold enough, or foolish enough, to take a group of kids on an excursion either at home or abroad, one must be prepared for absolutely any eventuality. In such circumstances, social class and family background count for nothing."

As I took a sip of the delicious brew, I caught Jim giving Henry a surreptitious wink.

"You are not convinced, are you, you cynical devils? Make yourselves comfortable and I'll give you an instance of something that happened at least twenty years after the jaunt to the seaside. You both know Lea Grange. If you don't, you ought to. (Henry was a member of the Governors and Jim's daughter, Sylvia, had been with us for three years.) It's not a bad school, is it? Quite good, in fact; excellent parental support, relatively well-behaved students...agreed? Well, five years ago, Jane and I agreed to join with a couple of members of staff and take a group of boys to Italy. With the advantage of past experience, it was planned right down to the finest detail so that nothing, absolutely nothing, could go wrong.

Our educational aims were threefold, the highlight being a tour of Pompeii, supplemented by a trip up Vesuvius, and a study of everyday life in one of our European neighbours. If we could fit in a visit to the Isle of Capri and a couple of days on a beach, what more could one desire?

A great deal of research, collated at regular intervals over the meat-balls and chips of the school midday meal, pointed us towards a small, family run hotel on the Amalfi coast. The place was described as idyllic and it seemed perfect for our purpose. Not only was the location most convenient for our sightseeing, it would also afford a wonderful base for relaxation on our rest days.

Satisfied that we had done all we could to ensure a profitable and enjoyable experience for our pupils, we selected a suitable week in the midsummer holidays and we placed a booking with a 'reputable' school excursion company. Everyone was happy: the kids with the optimism and exuberance characteristic of youth; their parents anticipating a week free of parenting, in some cases, a second honeymoon; and my two colleagues because, like Jane and me, they were confident that the time and thought that we all had devoted to planning would enable us also to enjoy the experience.

The first cloud appeared on the horizon when we were blandly informed that our chosen hotel had cancelled our booking owing to 'a recent horrendous experience' with another English school and that they flatly refused to reconsider. However, our caring excursion company, through its 'persistence emanating from a conscientious consideration for our well-being', had succeeded in obtaining accommodation at an even better hotel in Sorrento. The assurance that we would be more conveniently situated for Pompeii and Vesuvius carried less weight than the irrefutable fact that we had no alternative but to agree to the change, which we did under mild protest.

We certainly did not bargain for what followed by return of post. The hotel in Sorrento, the only one available at such short notice, could not take us until a week after the original date. The ramifications of this were far more serious than a mere change in our location and accommodation, however annoyed we were about that. The greatest difficulty was the fact that several parents had booked a short break to coincide with getting their loved ones off their hands. The response was mixed: resignation from those parents who were not affected unduly and anger from those who saw their second honeymoon disappear into thin air. Eight boys were withdrawn, leaving us with a total of thirty-three, including our two youngest sons.

By now, my attitude to, and dealings with, the holiday company had undergone a radical transformation. Innocuous chatter with their representatives about the weather, the state of one's health, the efficiency of one's motor-car and even the rate of growth of one's lawn gave way to basic courtesy tinged with suspicion. Thus, when the arrival airport was altered from Naples to Rome, I experienced no difficulty whatsoever in relaying the most ferocious insults about the company and its incompetent staff that my battered brain could muster. Perhaps it was this angry tirade that squeezed a concession that undoubtedly saved the holiday: the coach and driver who were to take us from Rome to our hotel in Sorrento were to be at our disposal throughout our stay in Italy.

That ended our communication with the company so at least no further problems emanated from that source. However, the final run up to the holiday was not completely trouble-free. Two days before departure, a fourteen-year-old member of our party injured himself in a bicycle accident and required several stitches in his stomach. He would be allowed to travel but his stitches would need to be taken out whilst we were in Italy. Fortunately, we had arranged for all the party to complete the medical form E11."

My two companions had been remarkably quiet and when their glasses were empty, Henry silently indicated his offer to buy the next round by a deft gesture with the stem of his pipe.

"No thanks, I've had enough; you two go ahead. To return to

my account, fellows, I trust you realise that, so far, we had not taken a single step on our journey. By now, I was begging the departure date to arrive, not because I was anticipating pleasure but simply so that no further problems could befall us before we were on our way! I shall not bore you with a detailed account of the journey to our hotel save to say that we experienced several delays capped by a tedious coach ride from Rome to Sorrento, where we finally arrived in the early hours of the morning, fraught, fatigued and fed up.

The entrance to the hotel had been so unobtrusive that Antonio, our driver, passed it twice before he realised that a single doorway was the sole way into the tiny square lobby, which afforded access to the smallest elevator that I have ever seen. It is no exaggeration to say that there was room only for one fat person or two thin persons or one thin person and a suitcase. The importance of the lift became apparent when we discovered that the hotel was situated on top of four storeys of shops and offices, the only alternative means of access being via a narrow spiral staircase. The logistical problem of moving thirty-three teenagers and four adults, plus personal luggage, from the cobbled street to the reception desk was challenging, particularly at half-past two in the morning. Whilst the younger ones, tearful with tiredness waited in line to take the lift, the older boys trundled upwards and upwards, round and round the half-lit stairs to reach the top, breathless with effort and not a little anger. When eventually we all crushed into the minute reception area, the owner passed a sardonic eye over our bedraggled, motley crew and, addressing me, announced, 'Please, make into two sixes and four fives.'

I was still deciding what he meant and how to ask him in Italian to repeat his request when Jane leaned over and whispered in my ear, 'It's the rooms; he wants you to arrange the boys into two sets of six and four batches of five.'

'But we booked double rooms!'

'That was in Amalfi,' she reminded me.

I turned to the owner, my dislike of him rapidly developing into hatred. 'Don't you mean six sets of two and five sets of four?'

'No signor...' At this point Antonio, my only link with the wretched holiday company intervened.

'Eets OK. We take a look. Very nice hotel.'

The owner, grateful for the support, attempted to resume control. 'Si Signor. You look - very nice big rooms.'

His idea of size differed greatly from mine and if the groans of the boys were any indication, from their perceptions of relative proportion! In fact, the rooms with five beds were just about acceptable but those designated for six persons were furnished, or should I say crammed, with three double bunks and nothing else. Apart from allocating the larger rooms to the older boys, I allowed the group to decide with whom they would share. It was well over an hour after our arrival that we settled down for what remained of the night. I trust that the kids were too exhausted to be disturbed every hour by the loud clanging of a nearby church clock. For myself, I can confirm that it was in perfect working order and that it did not once fail to strike on time!

It would be churlish to say that everything about the hotel was bad. The greatest advantage was that the bedrooms opened out on to a large roof terrace, the fourth side of which was enclosed by ornate iron railings over-looking a bustling street of shops, cafes, and ice-cream parlours. A covered area at one end, divided from the rest by a row of pot plants, was set out for dining, whilst the remainder was furnished with small tables and plastic chairs.

As the week progressed, Antonio's value developed from extremely useful to irreplaceable. I have already referred to his contribution in diffusing the tension when we were introduced to our accommodation. On our first morning, which was to be a rest day, he arranged to take us to a delightful little place on the Amalfi coast, where there was a lovely beach and safe swimming. By the time we returned for our evening meal, we were all in a far better frame of mind.

He was an immediate hit with all the boys and, when the time came for us to bid him arrivederci, they could all pronounce his favourite, if somewhat over-used word: Ciao. He was a careful shepherd on our excursions to Pompeii and Vesuvius and, in addition to producing other beaches for our rest days, he organised a visit to the Isle of Capri. Here, through an old army companion, he arranged for us to have the use of a private beach complete with toilets and changing accommodation."

At this stage, Jim could not resist, "It doesn't sound too bad to me. Pompeii, Vesuvius, Capri...free transport laid on; Henry and I would spend a fortune going to just one of those places."

His sly grin was not reciprocated by his companion who had a kinder nature and who, I suspect, was concerned that Jim was going a bit too far with the teasing. He averted his eyes, adjusted his tie, cleared his throat nervously, and then reached forward for his drink.

"Yes, it does sound attractive," I agreed, "but when did you last take thirty-three unpredictably behaved youngsters on holiday, acting as nursemaid to them for twenty-four hours every day? Homesickness, minor illnesses - all these have to be reckoned with. Getting the stitches removed from the young lad's stomach was easy compared with some problems that had to be dealt with."

Henry's next question was genuinely uncontroversial. "Oh yes, Adam. What happened about that?"

"In actual fact, it presented no problem. A couple of blocks from the hotel, in a walk-in medical centre, a giant-sized black-bearded doctor, clad in a beautiful white starched suit, put us at ease in his best broken English by asserting that Dino Zoff, the Italian goalkeeper was far better than Gordon Banks had ever been. Before I realised what was happening, the boy was assuring him that he hadn't felt a thing. We all shook hands, our offer of payment was waved away, and I was very impressed with what I had seen of the Italian heath service.

Returning to the theme that taking a bunch of kids on a school trip is not as easy as it may seem, the point is that you accept responsibility for their well-being and safety yet it is not humanly possible to watch them every minute of every day. Take Tim and Robert for instance; both have grown up into responsible adults. Tim is an officer in naval intelligence and Robert has recently qualified as a doctor yet they both courted death on the Italian trip. They could have disappeared without trace. The blame would have rested on my shoulders even though I would have been helpless to prevent the tragedy."

The legal implications of all this inspired Henry's next question. "How can you be sure, Adam? Lost without your knowledge?"

"Because the little brats sneaked out of the hotel at midnight and went for a swim in the Bay of Naples. We had been back at school for two weeks before I even heard about the escapade."

"Boys will be boys," joked Jim.

"Maybe, but what if one of them had been your young Jimmy? Don't deny that you would have held me responsible."

"Technically, you would have been unless you could have shown that all reasonable precautions had been taken," was the opinion proffered by our learned friend.

Meanwhile, I was heartened that Jim had been reached. "Whether or not Adam was legally responsible is not the point, Henry. If the lads had drowned, even though he was not at fault, it would have destroyed him."

The thought of that eventuality still sends a shiver down my spine. I hate to dwell upon it, so I moved on.

"The journey home was no picnic although I must admit that the detour via Monte Cassino was a bonus. Everybody was exhausted by the long coach journey before we even set foot on the plane and our flight home turned into one of the most terrifying experiences of my life. We shared the aeroplane with a girls' school from Wales and the fact that the flight consisted mainly of children, many of whom had not flown before that holiday, only contrived to make matters worse. Almost immediately after taking off, we encountered unremitting bad weather. Streaks of lightning appeared to flash from wing to wing via the interior of the cabin. The little aircraft was severely buffeted by the strong winds and had to fight continuously to hold its course. The atmosphere of terror that gripped its young passengers was something I would not want to experience ever again!

'Sell us your crucifix, Tim. I'll give you double what you paid,' one scared-to-death thirteen-year-old implored the midnight bather, who had made the recent purchase at Monte Cassino.

'Please, Sir, a girl at the back has filled seven sick bags,' was the reassuring snippet of information to which I was treated by another of my flock.

We circled, crossing over the angry white foam of the south coast three times before it was deemed fit for us to land which, by some miracle, we eventually did on to a flooded runway at least an inch deep in water. I remember Jane asking a stewardess if she had ever before encountered such horrendous conditions. 'Never, ever,' was her telling reply! Predictably, the delay caused us to miss our connection from Euston so we arrived in Beckbridge well after midnight several hours behind schedule. The anxious parents greeted us with a mixture of relief and anger. I was not in a mood to engage in social chitchat. I gave a brief explanation as to why we were so late, leaving the kids to fill in the details for their mums and dads. I had then made a hasty departure to my bed.

That was Henry's cue. "I must do the same...make a quick exit, I mean. Muriel stressed that we shall be eating at eight o'clock and she does not like to be kept waiting," said he, rising as he buttoned his gabardine.

"Me too, thanks for the entertainment, Adam. By the way, I hope you don't take everything I say too seriously!" grinned his fishing companion.

POSTSCRIPT TO CHAPTER FOURTEEN

At the beginning of this chapter, I referred to that exquisite market town, Kirkby Lonsdale where, during the late thirties and early forties, I had the good fortune to be educated. My thoughts took me back there to that glorious summer of 1941, to the early days of the Second World War. France had capitulated, the Low Countries had been overrun, Quisling had handed Norway to the Nazis and America was still neutral. Britain stood alone against Hitler's mighty army, which was poised to attack us from across the English Channel. Yet, two hundred miles away on the cricket field of my old school, it had been a tranquil, sunny Saturday afternoon.

The annual match against Kendal Grammar School had just ended in our favour. I had taken five wickets for twelve runs and hit my highest score ever with the bat. I was euphoric as I mounted my silver-blue Sun Wasp bicycle, the one with yellow tape wrapped around its drop handlebars. I could not wait to get home so that I could relate every detail of my success to my family.

The seven-mile ride would take me down the hill to the main square and over the River Lune before the climb at the other side of town would demand some effort from my tired legs. So, in my breathless haste, although the first mile was downhill, I pedalled furiously past the municipal library towards the town centre.

As I approached the bend in the road from where I could look down to the market square, I heard the strains of a military band playing, 'We're going to hang out the washing on the Zeigfreid Line, Have you any dirty washing, Mother dear?'

Rounding the bend at breakneck speed, I was aware of red, white, and blue flags flashing by. In the distance, there was a line of people marching across the T-junction at the bottom of the hill. Bunting was all around me, to both sides and overhead, draped across the pathetic lamp-posts that the blackout had rendered redundant for the duration.

At that point the incline of the hill suddenly increased, prompting me to take immediate action to adjust my speed to a manageable rate. I already knew that my front brake was out of action so, if I was to avoid a pile-up with the moving human wall, which was rapidly approaching, I must apply the brake on my rear wheel without further delay.

It may be that I snatched at the chromium lever and caught the flimsy threads of the calliper system unawares. Perhaps, like those on the front brake, they were well worn and overdue for replacement. All I remember is hearing the dreaded 'twang' as the cable snapped and rather than slowing, my machine propelled me at ever-increasing speed towards the boy scouts, the girl guides and the members of numerous voluntary organisations, all of whom were marching in the 'Wings for Victory' parade to raise money for our valiant Royal Air Force.

My first instinct was to lean forward and press the white plastic mudguard on to the front wheel. This substitute braking system had served me with some success on a couple of occasions in the past but never at the reckless speed that I had reached on that balmy evening. Before my stratagem began to have any effect, the friction resulting from the mudguard being pressed against the rapidly rotating tyre burned my hand, causing me to abandon my last chance of slowing down. By now, I was almost upon the junction. "Move out! Clear the way!" I yelled at the top of my voice. Fortunately, at that very moment, a Company of the local Boy's Brigade was passing in front of me. I had no time to dwell on the fact that it could have been so much worse - it could have been a group of World War One veterans, trundling along with their walking canes. Thankfully it was not and, by a combination of nifty footwork and incredible luck, the lads parted their ranks to let me through.

Meanwhile the onlookers were waving their arms furiously in my direction, shaking their fists and uttering a barrage of unprintable expletives. I have a slight recollection of being struck on the head and shoulders by the walking sticks of a couple of irate pensioners who, fortunately, were no longer as agile as they had been when they won the medal ribbons that were emblazoned on their jackets.

Two members of the constabulary ran towards me, holding their helmets tight to their heads. "Grab that lad!" shouted one.

"Stop the beggar!" bawled the other.

I did not linger to reply. This was not the appropriate moment to apologise. The prospect of a visit to the police station did not appeal to me; even worse, I did not fancy being the principal guest of a lynch mob. The road around the town square had levelled out and I had recovered control of my bicycle, which had suddenly undergone a change from the *raison d'etre* of my embarrassment to my only means of survival. It was to my advantage that I knew the layout of the buildings. A few yards in front of me was a narrow gap, known as a 'ginnel' in those parts. It led directly to the meadows by the River Lune...and to relative safety. Certainly, it was not my direct route home but it was the best means of escape from the turmoil I had caused. If I were to be brought to account, surely it would be in my interest to let the anger subside!

It goes without saying that the shine had been removed from my recent sporting achievement. After all, if I had been out for a 'duck' and taken no wickets that afternoon, I should not have been hurrying home in the first place. I was a victim of circumstance! Is it any wonder that I empathise with many of the recalcitrant characters that appear in these pages?

CHAPTER FIFTEEN

'Variety's the very spice of life,
That gives it all its flavour.'

William Cowper.

"I'm sorry, the Headmaster has just stepped out," said a voice on the telephone from somewhere in Salford.

"Is he expected back this afternoon?" My question should have been unnecessary; an efficient receptionist would have included the information in her initial message. Her response to my follow-up enquiry confirmed her unfitness to be the first point of contact in any organisation, especially a school, where reassuring the public is essential.

"Oh yes, he'll only be a few minutes. He's just popped out to look at the fire engines. He loves fire engines. He calls them his big red machines."

"Fire engines? Red machines?"

"Yes, there's a fire at the mill down the road. Three engines have already gone clanging past the school. He was really excited when he rushed out." A pause, then even worse, "He should be taking scripture with Three Remove but I've asked the Deputy to take over. He's a rum one is our Headmaster!"

"Thank you, no, I shan't trouble him to call me. I'll ring back in half an hour."

"He'll be back by then...unless they haven't managed to put the fire out, of course."

"Of course!"

As I carefully replaced my telephone, why was I not collapsing in fits of laughter? Why was I so depressed? To the average layman, the conversation to which I had just been a party would have been a very funny exchange, yet it had left me feeling sad. Sad because it served only to strengthen my belief that if education was to keep pace with the demands of the modern world, then a serious examination of the way schools are managed was required.

Thirty or forty years ago, when less than a fifth of our children were privileged enough to receive an academic education, a head teacher could take morning assembly, wander wistfully round the school back to his comfortable study and then only expect to have *The Times* crossword interrupted either by the direst emergency or his mid-morning cup of coffee. Not so now: with the post-war birth rate explosion, together with the realisation that almost all pupils are capable of obtaining some qualifications, schools have been allowed to grow out of all proportion. They can no longer be run by 'off the cuff' methods. A great deal of thought, and formal training in management, is needed.

Meanwhile, a few basic precepts for all heads to consider should begin with the acknowledgement that they alone are not the sole possessors of wisdom and knowledge. There is a need to listen to colleagues, to weigh their advice, to consider carefully and then to act positively and decisively...oh, and to make sure that the person manning the school telephone possesses an intelligence quotient of, at least, average standard!

I have a theory that the consummate power enjoyed by head teachers fosters the delusion that they are infallible, this being the greatest hindrance to their effectiveness. Whilst self-belief is essential, misplaced self-confidence is a handicap. I once worked for such a person, a decisive leader, thoughtful and dedicated, yet he could not bring himself to accept the advice of his subordinates. He was the ideal personification of the maxim: 'You can always tell a Yorkshireman...but you can't tell him much!' On one occasion, when he was reversing his car in a tight situation he backed into a bollard completely ignoring the loud cries imploring him to stop. The trouble was that the person warning him was a newly appointed teacher and the man of importance refused to be advised by such a lowly fellow.

I was once personally involved when his delusion of importance led to his considerable embarrassment. It happened one Wednesday afternoon. I remember the particular day of the week because that was his secretary's day off; otherwise, the problem would not have occurred.

Although his behaviour to all members of staff was ever courteous and proper, it was quite apparent to everyone that he was very fond of his young secretary. I suppose it was true to say that she could 'twist him round her little finger'. Not without cause, he trusted her implicitly and, although she was popular with the rest of the staff, it was mildly resented by some that he appeared to heed her advice whilst he would disregard that of everyone else including very senior professional colleagues. Of course, a method to circumvent this difficulty was eventually devised: the sure way of getting him to adopt a suggestion was to ask the young secretary to put it forward! One particular way her favoured status manifested itself was in the arrangement he had devised for her to summon him to his study, should he be required urgently when he was wandering about the school. On such occasions, she would alert him by three short bursts on the electric bell, the bell that was used otherwise to regulate the times of lessons.

On that particular Wednesday afternoon, I was searching for some information in the school library, which was across the entrance hall from the Head's study, when an erudite looking stranger entered. Having complained that he had been unable to obtain a response either from the secretary's room or the Head's, he introduced himself as the new Government Inspector for our district. The importance of his status merited immediate action and I did not have to ponder long on how to solve the difficulty. I assured our visitor that the Head would be with us in no time at all as I gave the famous bell three sharp prods. Of course, I had not taken account of my master's psychological hang-up. When he heard the three peals, his initial reaction was to respond with haste to his loyal secretary's summons, only to realise that it was her day off. How dare anyone else use their private means of communication! So the signal was ignored.

The inspector, clearly agitated at being kept waiting for ten minutes or so, suggested that we both should go in separate directions to look for the elusive Head. I refused to contemplate our illustrious visitor being exposed to such inconvenience, indeed not! I promised that I would make the signal work this time and I made sure it did by repeating it at ten-second intervals.

This resulted in several adjacent classroom doors being flung open as anxious teachers enquired if it was the fire alarm. Mercifully, before a mass evacuation of the premises got under way, a very red-faced and angry Headmaster appeared at the far end of the corridor and hurried along towards us. Before my breathless boss could utter a word, I called out the identity of our visitor. Then I made a strategic retreat whilst the two of them were still shaking hands.

If misplaced self-importance resulted in nothing worse than a red face there would be no cause for alarm. Sadly, a refusal to heed the advice of others usually has more dire consequences. The most extreme example of this, in my experience, concerned a fourteen-year-old schoolboy, whom I shall call Sidney and a Lincolnshire Headmaster, whom I have never met.

To call Sidney a misfit is not an exaggeration. Undersized for his age, thin, bespectacled, with prominent teeth that pleaded for a course of orthodontistry, he was treated as an outcast by members of his age group. This had worrying consequences in that it encouraged him to express himself in the way that came most naturally to him, that is, to be deceitful and disruptive. This behaviour appealed to a small group of younger boys who provided the friendship and attention that his peers denied him. His parents were not intellectually equipped to handle their problem child - if his brains were hereditary then the source must have resided in a generation long passed.

His father was a blustering, loud-mouthed, uncouth creature, well acquainted with the insides of the local pubs, particularly over the past six months since the slipper works had laid him off. It was rumoured that he would never again be employed in the Beckbridge Valley. Sidney's mother, in contrast, was a timid, downtrodden, undernourished little lady, utterly unable to cope with the two males in her life, in spite of devoting all her waking hours to the impossible task.

Unfortunately, Sidney's misdemeanours were not confined to mere disruption. On more than one occasion he was caught committing acts of vandalism and, over the years, we received a succession of complaints from the occupants of the old peoples' bungalows nearby, about both his damage to plants and his insolence and bad language when he was chastised. To my knowledge he had received at least one official police caution for loitering with intent in the local supermarket. In short, he was a thoroughly bad example to other boys, particularly to those younger and less intelligent than he.

Therefore, I confess that I was not unduly sorry when Sidney's mother informed Bernie Lord, his Head of Year, that the family would be leaving Beckbridge at the end of the week. Her husband's brother had spoken for him and he had obtained work in a local steelworks. In addition, Scunthorpe council had allocated them a maisonette.

I cannot explain why I linked this gem of welcome news with a seemingly unconnected report I received from Bill Brown, the school keeper, two days later.

"We were burgled last night. Whoever 'done' it knew their way about...got in through the boys' toilets. I'm sure I fastened all the window catches but I must have missed one."

"Any damage? Anything missing?"

"Yes and no: no damage but four or five boxes of Jammy Dodgers have gone."

I knew then why he had described it as an inside job. The unlocked toilet window could have been the result of a mistake but discovering where the biscuits were kept was no accident. The tuck shop store was in the roof space above the side entrance. Access to the goodies was via a pull-down ladder attached to a trap door in the ceiling. Most of our pupils knew where the biscuits were stored but no intruder would have dreamed of looking there.

"Have you any idea who might have done it, Bill?" He was the obvious starting point for any investigation. He was first on the scene, his house overlooked the back of the school building and, most important of all, he was the possessor of a shrewd and suspicious brain.

"Not really. Just before I locked up I shifted that little group of new kids that are rapidly developing into a bunch of thugs. You'll have to sort them out before long!"

Was he referring to Sidney's hangers-on? I made a mental note of his advice as I enquired, "Anybody else?"

"Not that I can recall; just four or five young nippers."

That was all. I thought about informing the police but decided against it. At one time I would not have rested until I had tracked down the culprit. Was I getting too old for the job or too busy to immerse myself in detective work? I was sure of one thing: in future, Bill Brown would make certain that all window catches were secure...at least for the next few weeks!

I was clearing my desk on that Friday afternoon when, of all people, Sidney appeared at my door. "I've come to say goodbye and to thank you for everything you have done for me and my family, Sir."

Here I should explain that, in spite of all his faults, Sidney was perhaps the most polite child that I have ever come across. Of course, it was a facade to cover his villainous instincts, which lurked just below the surface, ever ready to take advantage of any sucker who fell for his charm. So I suppose that I was on my guard when I detected a slight change in the normal pitch of his voice, a kind of triumphalist tone. Were my suspicions of the boy becoming obsessive? Yet there was undoubtedly something indefinable in his body language that did not ring true.

"That's very thoughtful of you, Sidney. Let me see, where are you moving to?"

"Scunthorpe, Sir. It's a manufacturing town in Lincolnshire, mainly steel."

"Yes, I do know that, Sidney."

"Well, goodbye, Sir."

"Goodbye Sidney...wait, sit down a moment. You may be able to give me one last bit of help before you leave us."

"I...help you, Sir?" Imperiousness tinged with a modicum of humility!

"Yes, you Sidney. Somebody broke into the school last night. Have you any idea who it could be?"

"Me, Sir? No, of course not, Sir. Oh dear, I am so sorry. Fancy stealing from one's own school!"

"I did not say that anything had been taken, Sidney, and we don't know that it was one of our pupils."

The lad maintained eye contact but he failed to suppress the slight flush. He scratched his left calf with his right instep.

"No, Sir, of course we don't. May I ask if anything was taken?"

"Before we get on to that, young man, I want to know if you were on the school premises last night."

His eyes did not flicker but he moistened the front of his protruding molars. He was well aware that Bill Brown's bedroom windows overlooked the school.

"Me, Sir? As a matter of fact, Sir, now you mention it, Sir, I did revisit the grounds for a short time...just to have a last look at my school. Wait a minute, Sir. I do remember seeing some older boys hanging about. They were strangers to me. They looked very, very suspicious." Clearly an attempt to divert my line of questioning … which I did not buy. At the same time, he was not succumbing to my bluff. I decided on a more direct approach.

"I don't suppose that you were offered any biscuits last night?"

"Biscuits, Sir? Indeed no, Sir." I maintained my fixed gaze as he scratched his ear, then continued, "In any case, I would not have accepted them. I never eat Jammy Dodgers!"

The brand of biscuits had not been mentioned! So Sid was the culprit yet I was still without proof...and without time to find any. "I think you know more about this than you are admitting, Sidney."

Whilst he vociferously protested his innocence, I placed him in the charge of David James. I then telephoned the police station and asked for Detective Charlton.

Twenty minutes later I had recounted the facts to him as he leaned against the mantelpiece in my study. In short, I was in no doubt whatsoever that Sidney had stolen the biscuits and I feared that he had involved some of his young admirers. I wanted him exposed and I wanted my biscuits but most of all, I wanted to show his inexperienced imitators that crime does not pay, especially at Lea Grange! That was all I wanted; I did not wish to press charges.

"You say they are leaving tomorrow. That doesn't leave us much time."

Neither of us spoke for a while. I was almost considering thumbscrews when my friend surprised me with, "I'll show him the inside of a police cell. That usually makes an impression!" Then, "You get a message to his parents. Tell them he's been arrested on suspicion of theft."

"That's going a bit far, isn't it, Bobby? I expected you to give him a good talking to here."

"Look, Adam, we know he's got the biscuits hidden away somewhere. From what you tell me, he won't own up easily, especially as he knows that by this time tomorrow he'll be miles away from Beckbridge. I shan't do anything improper - trust me."

I did trust him but to be on the safe side I went personally to Sidney's home. Predictably, father was 'out' so, feeling very uncomfortable but determined to go through with the chosen course of action, I drove mum down to the police station and left her with her protesting son.

On the stroke of nine o'clock, my depression was lifted by a single telephone call from Bobby Charlton. "You were right, Adam! It was him and we've got five boxes of Jammy Dodgers to prove it...and he's come clean in front of his parents. Yes, they are both here. It was when his father turned up worse for drink that Sidney's brave act capitulated."

"It's taken enough of your time, my friend. How did you finally get him to confess?"

"I told him and his parents that we were sure that he had got the biscuits and that he would not be going anywhere until they were given back. I deliberately avoided talking about theft or breaking in. I just kept on about the missing biscuits. Then, about an hour ago, I told them that you would not press charges if he owned up - I hope that's still the case - but that I would charge him with wasting police time if he messed me about much longer.

Suddenly he shrugged and said, 'You win, Inspector.' The little bugger knows I'm only a constable!"

The Lincolnshire Headmaster entered the saga the moment I realised that we had forwarded Sidney's records without indicating the size of the potential problem we had inflicted upon the unfortunate fellow. At the very least, I felt that I should have warned him of the boy's tendency to use good manners as a cover for his sinister behaviour. I suppose I was still smarting from the bold and cheeky way he had called in to see me on that last Friday afternoon, obviously with the intention of having a laugh at my expense. I hope not. I would prefer to believe that it was Sidney's likely corrupting influence on the unsuspecting youngsters of Scunthorpe that motivated me to alert his new Head to his remarkable gift for deception.

"Good morning, my name is Adam Firestone speaking from Lea Grange School, Lancashire. I understand that you have just admitted one of my old pupils." I followed with Sidney's full name.

"Yes, in actual fact I saw him myself, this morning...a delightful chappie: not blessed with the best of looks, hey, but very articulate. You must have a good set of English teachers!"

That sounded like Sidney. Should I spoil the illusion? Of course I should. That was the whole purpose of my call. It was my duty to a fellow professional.

"Well, yes, he is very articulate, that is true...and extremely well-mannered. In fact, that is why I am speaking to you. I don't quite know how to say this but please do not allow yourself to be deceived by his facade of politeness. The boy is fundamentally a villain, a likeable one maybe, but unless he is carefully watched, he will be a very bad influence on younger boys." There was no response from Scunthorpe. "Are you still there?" I enquired.

There was hostility in the voice that eventually answered me. "I don't want to hear this. I wish that you had not bothered to phone if all you can do is blacken the boy's character before he has had a chance to prove himself here. Mine is a very forward-looking school, Mr. Firestone. We are proud of the progress we make with our students."

"Then there's nothing more to say."

"That's right. Goodbye."

Regrettably, I am unable to report further on Sidney. I suppose that I shall never know how he turned out, although Bernie Lord assured me that he recognised him among the demonstrators on the roof of Strangeways Prison, who were fleetingly shown on Granada Television at the time of the last riot. I hope that Bernie was mistaken and that my counterpart in Scunthorpe worked a miracle and reformed Sidney. With hindsight, I am satisfied that I did my duty by sounding a warning and I trust that the Lincolnshire Head's self-belief did not end up as a case of self-delusion!

It goes without saying that all successful Headteachers have their own special way of projecting their image. I have already written about the 'Spotlight Head', whom I classify as an extreme case of eccentricity, but close behind him in the absurdity stakes would feature the Head of a Boys' Grammar School I once had dealings with.

The fact that it was a single-sex school is of considerable significance. Many people in education feel that boys benefit from being educated along with girls, although they are quick to assert that the reverse is not true. Apparently, the feminine influence has a restraining influence on the worst excesses of the males! Some go as far as to make the incongruous statement that boys should be taught in mixed classes whilst girls should be educated in all-female groups!

The particular school about which I am writing was crying out for a female input. The boys were rowdy and ill disciplined, the premises were shabby and untidy, litter was present in abundance, and graffiti and vandalism were both far too much in evidence

'Squeers', the Headmaster, as he was known to all and sundry, was never seen anywhere without his academic gown, and outdoors he always added his mortar-board and carried his shooting stick. "What is so unusual about that," one may ask. "It does no harm to dress for the part, does it?" No, of course not, but there was more to it than just dressing up. There was something indefinably bizarre about his whole demeanour, in his day to day behaviour.

I well remember visiting his school to view a new piece of apparatus he had recently installed in his technical studies suite.

"Come along, Firestone (we were never on first-name terms), we can call in on the rabbits; it's on our way to the workshops," he announced, planting his cap firmly on his bald pate before selecting his shooting stick from an ornate umbrella stand.

Whilst I was still pondering whether 'rabbits' was his term for eleven-year-old boys or whether he really meant Angoras and such like, my nostrils solved the puzzle as we drew near to the biology block. Once through the outside doors, we were in a large lobby, which housed several animal cages to which Squeers seemed magnetically drawn in spite of the putrid odours they were emitting.

After articulating a series of weird sounds, unintelligible to me but presumably understood by his little friends in the cages, he suddenly turned to me and explained, "I love every one of them...come on, Firestone, we'd better let Jenkins know we've been in."

The person of whom he spoke was obviously teaching in the classroom furthest down the corridor because my host led me towards a door near the end. He knocked loudly, then made several attempts to turn the knob, all without success. Eventually deciding to abandon the hopeless task, he took four or five steps further along the corridor and halted opposite a large hole in the plasterboard wall, clearly the result of vandalism. It was more than three feet square and about two feet up from the floor.

My host stood motionless for a while, carefully weighing up the situation then, without further ado, he leaned his stick against what remained of the damaged wall, clasped one hand on to his mortar-board, lifted up the bottom of his gown and made a majestic entrance through the wall. I was left with no option but to follow by the same method although, being much taller, I did so with some difficulty.

The reaction of the pupils said it all. As one, they looked up from their work and, apart from a few sly grins, they took no notice, clearly indicating that nothing Squeers did, however outlandish it might be, would surprise them.

I was reminded of my first Headmaster's advice, "You've either got to be severe with them or make out you're crazy." Poor old Squeers was a past master at the latter! Enough said.

I have deliberately left my final tale about a fellow Head until last because I enjoy recalling it more than any other. In this, I am not alone: it is the episode to which old students invariably refer and laugh about when I meet them, even years after they have departed Lea Grange.

Edith was Head of a nearby school when I first arrived in the Beckbridge Valley and we soon formed a working relationship. She was a stickler for high standards, a trait that endeared her to parents and senior students, although her strictness was not always to the liking of her younger pupils. Her philosophy was uncomplicated: instil the correct attitude in new entrants, then relax and let them enjoy the remainder of their schooling.

The incident that induced Edith and me to embark on a joint operation involved Tony, our barrel-chested centre forward, together with two girls and a lad from Edith's school. Tony's failure to turn up after the midday break was viewed with suspicion by his Form Tutor who, by pursuing his enquiries with vigour and skill, discovered that the little group had elected to spend the afternoon in the home of one of the girls.

Obviously, it is not humanly possible to prevent teenage boys and girls from getting into mischief in their own time but I was determined that my pupil would not do so when he should be in school. So I telephoned Edith, gave her the girls' names and waited whilst she looked up their addresses.

As Edith was as adamant as I that they should not succeed in their little scheme, she readily agreed to my suggestion that we should embark upon a rescue mission without delay. Ten minutes later, she sat in the passenger seat of my car as we sped towards the nearest address, a bungalow in a well-heeled part of town.

"Stop here, Adam, whilst we sort out our strategy. With luck, they are in there." She pointed to a bungalow about twenty yards further down the road.

"Right, Edith, you give me a couple of minutes to get round the back, then pound heavily on the front door."

By skirting round the bottom of adjacent gardens, bent double in commando style, I reached the rear of the target dwelling just as the rattling of the front door commenced. Cries of alarm, punctuated by expletives I had not heard since I was demobilised from the Air Force, preceded the flinging open of the back door to enable four terrified youngsters to pour straight out into my waiting arms.

"Back inside, all of you!"

I don't know whether Edith was genuinely angry or whether she was acting as she manhandled her three recalcitrant students before flinging them on to the sumptuous chairs of the well-furnished lounge. She then proceeded to harangue them unmercifully. Not to be outdone, I adopted my sternest image and ordered Tony to return to school as fast as his legs would carry him.

"Your punishment will be doubled if you are not waiting for me outside my study when I arrive back!" I called to the retreating figure as he disappeared in the direction of Lea Grange.

Many, many years later, Tony returned to his old school to discuss the entry of his eleven-year-old daughter. Over a cup of coffee, we reminisced about his prowess as our leading goal-scorer and, inevitably, we had a really good laugh about the bungalow incident.

"Tony, do you intend to come to the anniversary celebration next Thursday?"

"Yes, as a matter of fact, I've got two tickets…for my wife and me. I bought them just now from your secretary."

"Well, I'll let you into a little secret. I shall not be here when the next one comes around."

"Not here?"

"Don't worry, I'm not ill, I'm not about to die! No, I shall soon be retiring from Lea Grange and I want to make this year's function really special. I'm going to ask you a favour, Tony."

"Me? A favour?"

"Yes, you...during the evening I'm due to give a short talk about interesting incidents that have occurred over the years. I'd like to use the bungalow episode to start with, to get the audience in a happy frame of mind. Would you have any objection?"

"Not at all; plenty of people know about it."

"Yes, but I don't know your wife? I would not wish to embarrass you in front of her."

"Embarrass me! That's a laugh! You might think you don't know her but perhaps you'll recognise her when you see her. It was her house we went to. She was the one who'd suggested taking the afternoon off in the first place!"

This meeting confirmed my decision to retire. Although leaving Lea Grange was going to be a big wrench for me, Tony's visit to enrol his daughter had brought home how the years had flown. Forty years on, some of my first pupils would not only be parents: many would be taking pleasure in their grandchildren.

Yes, Adam, it's time to hang up your boots and make way for a youngster!

Also by the same author.

Head's Tales

The prequel to Still Ahead, available by special order from

Central Publishing Limited
Royd Street Offices
Milnsbridge
Huddersfield
HD3 4QY

£5.99 + P&P
Please allow 14 days for delivery.